Singapore Math®

Tests

4B

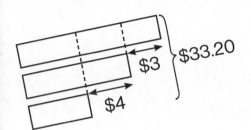

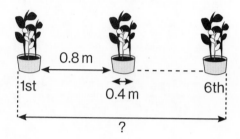

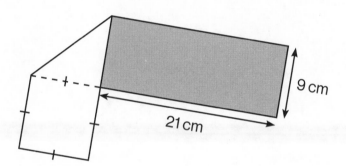

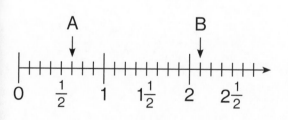

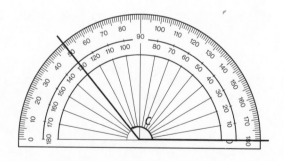

Differentiated Unit Tests
Continual Assessments

 Singapore Math Inc.®

BLANK

Preface

Singapore Math® Tests is a series of structured assessments to help teachers evaluate student progress. The tests align with the content of Primary Mathematics Common Core textbooks.

Each level offers differentiated tests (Test A and Test B) to suit individual needs. Tests consist of multiple-choice questions that assess comprehension of key concepts and free response questions that demonstrate problem solving skills. Three continual assessments cover topics from earlier units and a year-end assessment covers the entire curriculum.

Test A focuses on key concepts and fundamental problem solving skills.

Test B focuses on the application of analytical skills, thinking skills, and heuristics.

Contents

Tests 4B   © 2016 Singapore Math Inc.®

BLANK

Name: _____   Date: _____

Test A   **30 min**

60

Score

Unit 6 Decimals

Section A (2 points each)
Circle the correct option: **A**, **B**, **C**, or **D**.

1. In the decimal to the right, which digit is in the tenths place?

    43.58

    A 5   **B** 8

    C 3   **D** 4

2. What is the missing number?

    $$9.02 = 9 + \dfrac{2}{\boxed{?}}$$

    A 1   **B** 10

    C 100   **D** 1,000

3. Express the fraction on the card as a decimal.

    $5\dfrac{1}{4}$

    A 5.1   **B** 5.4

    C 5.14   **D** 5.25

4. Which of the following decimals is the greatest?

A

B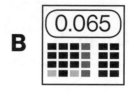

C

D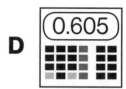

5. Express the decimal below as a fraction in its simplest form.

A $\frac{2}{25}$ **B** $\frac{4}{5}$ **C** $\frac{1}{80}$ **D** $\frac{1}{8}$

6. In 10.834, which digit is in the thousandths place?

A 10   **B** 4

C 8   **D** 3

7. What is the value of n in $1.45 = 1 + \dfrac{45}{n}$?

   A 10

   B 0.01

   C 100

   D 0.1

8. What number is 0.1 more than 234.56?

   A 234.57

   B 235.56

   C 234.156

   D 234.66

9. What is 10.785 rounded to the nearest hundredths place?

   A 10.79

   B 10.78

   C 10.8

   D 11

10. What is the missing number?
    32.235 is __?__ more than 32.23.

    A .05

    B .005

    C 5

    D .5

Section B (2 points each)

11. Write each fraction as a decimal.

    a. $\dfrac{17}{100}$ = _____

    b. $3\dfrac{1}{10}$ = _____

12. Express the following as a fraction in its simplest form.

    a) 1 dollar and 70 cents = _____

    b) 4 dollars and 2 cents = _____

13. Circle the values that are the same as "zero point nine".

    9.0 $\dfrac{9}{10}$ 9.1   nine tenths   0.9

14. Shade to show 0.62.

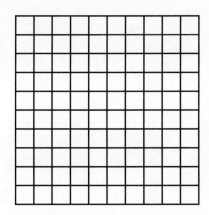

15. In which of the following numbers does the digit 4 stand for 4 tenths?

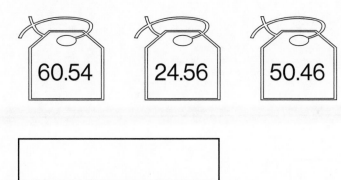

16. Write 15 thousandths as a decimal.

17.   Express the following as decimals.

a)   2 dollars and 65 cents = _____

b)   95 cents = _____

18.   What is the sum? Write it as a decimal.

$$7 + \frac{2}{10} + \frac{9}{1,000} = \boxed{}$$

19.   Express the decimal below as a fraction in its simplest form.

16.75

20.   Find the value of each of the following.

a) $72.83 + $0.05 = _____

b) $1.45 − $0.03 = _____

21. Fill in the boxes with the missing decimals.

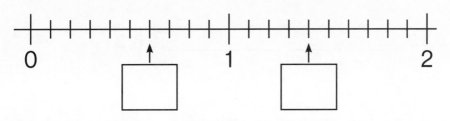

22. Arrange the following numbers in order from greatest to smallest.

_____, _____, _____

23. Arrange the numbers in decreasing order.

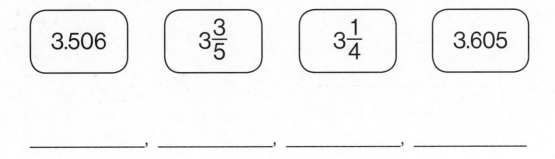

_____, _____, _____, _____

24. Complete the number pattern.

1.3, 1.6, 1.9, _____, _____, 2.8, 3.1

25. What is the length of the pencil? Give your answer as a decimal.

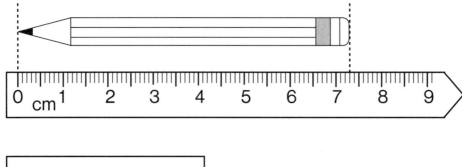

26. The mass of a package is 27.368 kg. Round the mass to the nearest tenth.

27. Which of the following numbers when rounded to 2 decimal places is 52.74? Circle your answer.

52.734   52.739   52.745   52.749

28. Write your answer as a decimal.

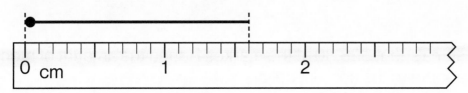

The length of the pin is _____ cm.

29.   Write your answer as a decimal.

The total volume of smoothie in these blenders is _____ L.

30.   Sushma spent $28.30 at the market. Round the amount of money she spent to the nearest dollar.

Name: _____ Date: _____

Test B  30 min

60
Score

Unit 6 Decimals

Section A (2 points each)
Circle the correct option: **A**, **B**, **C**, or **D**.

1. Which of the following numbers is the same as
   40 tens, 5 tenths and 9 thousandths?

   A 40.59   **B** 40.509

   C 45.009   **D** 400.509

2. What is the decimal represented by A?

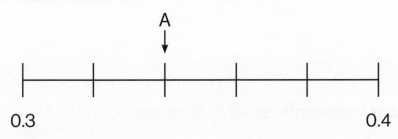

0.3   0.4

   A 0.302   **B** 0.304

   C 0.32   **D** 0.34

3. What is the missing sum?

$$16 + \frac{4}{5} + \frac{3}{40} = \boxed{ ? }$$

    A 16.875   **B** 16.6

    C 17.55   **D** 16.06

4. Which one of the following shows 7 dollars and 2 quarters as a decimal and a fraction in its simplest form?

    A \$7.50 and \$$7\frac{1}{2}$ **B** \$7.50 and \$$7\frac{1}{5}$

    C \$7.20 and \$$7\frac{1}{20}$ **D** \$7.25 and \$$7\frac{1}{2}$

5. Which number represents "seventy point one zero two"?

    A 70.102   **B** 70.12

    C 70.012   **D** 70.120

6. In which number does the digit 5 stand for 5 thousandths?

    A   24.512   **B**   87.05

    C   135.87   **D**   123.405

7. Which number represents seven and sixty-three hundredths?

    A   76.3   **B**   7.063

    C   7.63   **D**   763

8. What is the value of n in $0.83 = \dfrac{n}{10} + \dfrac{3}{100}$?

    A   8   **B**   3

    C   83   **D**   0.8

9. The distance between Jaret's house and Ocean Park is 8.398 km. What is the distance when rounded to 2 decimal places?

A 8.30 km

B 8.39 km

C 8.40 km

D 8.49 km

10. The cost of a science kit when rounded to the nearest dollar is $60. Which one of the following is the actual price of the science kit?

A $59.45

B $59.50

C $60.50

D $61.40

Section B (2 points each)

11. Shade to show 1.35.

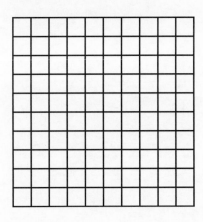 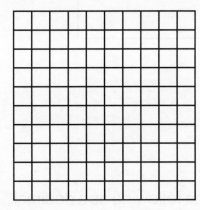

12. What is the number represented by the letter X?

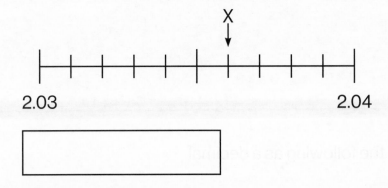

2.03   2.04

13. Write >, <, or =.

a) $0.01 _____ $\frac{2}{100}$ of $1

b) 1.1 kg _____ 11 g

14. How many hundredths make 3.05?

$$\boxed{}$$

15. Express the following as a decimal.

a) $52.70 + 5 cents = _____

b) 35.604 − 0.4 = _____

16. Write each of the following as a decimal.

a) 0.1 + .02 + 0.003 = _____

b) thirty-two and fifteen thousandths = _____

17. Arrange the following in decreasing order.

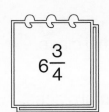 $6\frac{3}{4}$ 6.705    $6\frac{4}{5}$ 6.507

Answer:

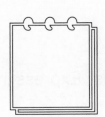   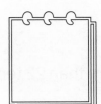      

18. Arrange the numbers in increasing order.

$5\frac{21}{25}$ 5.851 $5\frac{17}{20}$ 6.001

Answer:

19. A piece of wood is 0.495 cm thick. The estimated thickness of the piece of wood is:

a) _____ cm when rounded to 1 decimal place.

b) _____ cm when rounded to 2 decimal places.

20. What number is 9 hundredths more than 22 tenths? Express the answer as a decimal.

21. The mass of a fruit basket is 10.9 kg when rounded to 1 decimal place. What is the greatest possible mass of the fruit basket? Write your answer to 2 decimal places.

22. A bike helmet costs $37 when rounded to the nearest dollar. What is the lowest possible price of the bike helmet?

```
┌────────────────────┐
│                    │
│                    │
└────────────────────┘
```

23. Study the number pattern. Write the missing number.

5.07   4.67   4.37   4.07

24. Match the decimals with the mixed numbers.

1.4 ●	● $1\frac{1}{50}$
1.06 ●	● $1\frac{1}{25}$
1.5 ●	● $1\frac{1}{20}$
1.6 ●	● $1\frac{3}{50}$
1.08 ●	● $1\frac{2}{25}$
1.2 ●	● $1\frac{2}{5}$
1.02 ●	● $1\frac{4}{5}$
1.05 ●	● $1\frac{1}{2}$
1.8 ●	● $1\frac{3}{5}$
1.04 ●	● $1\frac{1}{5}$

25. The letters A and B each stand for a number on the number line below. What is the sum of A and B? Give your answer as a decimal.

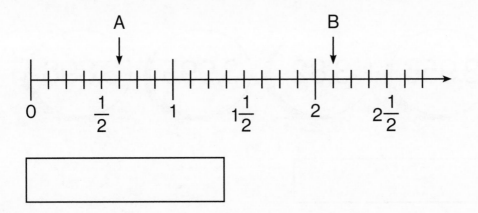

26. The mass of a bag of cement is 54.725 kg. The estimated mass of the bag of cement is:

a) _____ kg when rounded to the nearest kilogram.

b) _____ kg when rounded to 1 decimal place.

c) _____ kg when rounded to 2 decimal places.

27. One of the following numbers below gives the same value when rounded to the nearest whole number, tenth, and hundredth. What number is it?

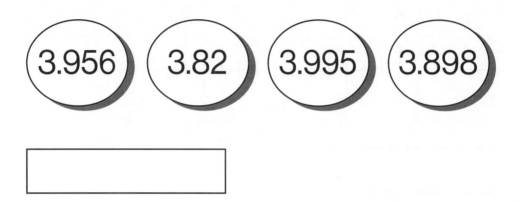

3.956   3.82   3.995   3.898

[ ]

28. Henry is making a number pattern as shown below.

2.6, 2.9, 3.2, 3.5, ... , 5.3

How many numbers are missing in the pattern?

[ ]

29. Read the clues carefully. Write the digits in the blanks.

The digit 0 is in the tenths place.
The digit 7 is in the hundredths place.
The digit in the ones place is 2 more than the digit in the tenths place.
The digit in the thousandths place is 2 less than the digit in the hundredths place.

_____ . _____ _____ _____

30. Arvind is 1.78 m tall. Justin is $1\frac{3}{4}$ m tall. Meiling is 1.8 m tall.

Who is the shortest? Who is the tallest?

_____ is the shortest.

_____ is the tallest.

BLANK

Name: _____ Date: _____

Test A **40 min**

60

Score

Section A (2 points each)
Circle the correct option: **A**, **B**, **C**, or **D**.

1. Add 0.5 to 3.21. What is the answer?

```
    3 . 2 1
  + 0 . 5
  _____
```

A 2.71   **B** 3.26

C 3.71   **D** 8.21

2. Subtract 5.4 from 8. What is the answer?

```
    8 . 0
  - 5 . 4
  _____
```

A 3.4   **B** 2.6

C 3.6   **D** 13.4

3. Multiply 22.04 by 7. What is the answer?

$$
\begin{array}{r}
2\ 2\ .0\ 4 \\
\times \qquad 7 \\
\hline
\\
\hline
\end{array}
$$

A 154.28   **B** 156.8

C 154   **D** 15,428

4. What is the sum of 5 tenths and 4 tenths?

A 9   **B** 90

C .09   **D** 0.9

5. What is the value of 35 ÷ 6 to 1 decimal place?

A 5.0   **B** 5.83

C 5.8   **D** 6.0

6. The missing number is __?__.

$$83.2 + 100 = \boxed{?} + 2.8$$

A 180.4   **B** 183.2

C 97.2   **D** 186

7. The missing number is __?__.

$$17.8 \times 5 = \boxed{?} \times 4$$

A 22.5   **B** 22.25

C 22   **D** 22.22

8. Lily mixed 3.2 liters of red paint with $1\frac{1}{4}$ liters of yellow paint to make orange paint. How many liters of orange paint did she make?

A 1.95 liters   **B** 4.34 liters

C 4.45 liters   **D** 4.61 liters

9. Bao bought 7 bags of green beans. The mass of each bag of green beans was 1.05 kg. How many kilograms of green beans did he buy altogether?

A 7.05 kg

B 7.35 kg

C 7.305 kg

D 73.5 kg

10. Joel paid $24.32 for 4 identical binders. What was the cost of each binder?

A $6.08

B $6.80

C $60.80

D $60.08

Section B (2 points each)

11. What is 7 tenths more than 8.96?

        ┌─────────────────────┐
        │   │
        │   │
        └─────────────────────┘

12. What is 9 hundredths less than 3.3?

        ┌─────────────────────┐
        │   │
        │   │
        └─────────────────────┘

13. Britta bought a burger and an ice-cream cone as priced below. How much did she pay altogether?

    $3.40 $0.75

        ┌─────────────────────┐
        │   │
        │   │
        └─────────────────────┘

14. How much more does the movie ticket cost than the tub of popcorn?

    $9.50 $4.70

        ┌─────────────────────┐
        │   │
        │   │
        └─────────────────────┘

15. Multiply 0.7 by 12. What is the product?

16. Divide 32 by 7 and round the quotient to one decimal place.

17. What is 64 hundredths ÷ 8?

18. Divide 21 hundredths by 3. What is the quotient?

19. Gabriel paid $50 for two of the following items. Which two items did he buy?

A: $32.15   **B:** $32.05   **C:** $18.95   **D:** $17.85

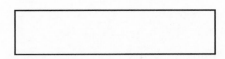

20. A book is sold for $7.45. Find the cost of 8 such books. Round your answer to the nearest dollar.

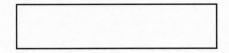

Section C (4 points each)

21. A roll of string was cut into 2 pieces. One piece was 3 times as long as the other piece. If the longer piece was 10.08 m long, what was the length of the shorter piece?

22. Diana bought 2 staplers at $3.05 each. She gave the cashier a $20 bill. How much change did she receive?

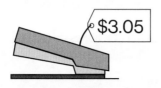
$3.05

23. Simon used 1.4 kg of clay to make a statue. He made 3 such statues. He had 10 kg of clay at first. What was the mass of clay he had left?

24. June prepared 5 L of lemonade. After she drank 0.96 L of the lemonade, she poured the remaining lemonade equally into 4 bottles. What is the volume of lemonade in each bottle?

25. In a supermarket, apples were sold at 6 for $5.80. Theresa wanted to buy 24 apples. How much would she have to pay for the apples?

Name: _____   Date: _____

Test B

40 min

<table><tr><td></td></tr><tr><td>60</td></tr></table>

Score

Unit 7 The Four Operations of Decimals

Section A (2 points each)
Circle the correct option: **A**, **B**, **C**, or **D**.

1. In the product of 2.45 and 3, what is the value of the digit 3?

$$
\begin{array}{r}
2.4\,5 \\
\times \quad\ \ 3 \\
\hline
\\
\hline
\end{array}
$$

   A 0.3   **B** 3

   C 30   **D** 300

2. Divide 0.74 by 5. What is the quotient when rounded to the nearest tenth?

   A 0.2   **B** 0.1

   C 0.15   **D** 0.14

3. What is the sum of 21 tenths and 21 hundredths?

    A 2.31   **B** 0.42

    C 0.042   **D** 2,121

4. Which of the following has the same value as 1 − 0.25?

    A 100 hundredths − 25 tenths

    B 100 hundredths − 25 tens

    C 10 tenths − 25 hundredths

    D 10 tenths − 25 tenths

5. 84.7 is ___?___ tenths more than 82.8.

    A 19   **B** 1.9

    C 1   **D** 9

6. A baker bought 25 kg of flour. After she had used 0.96 kg of the flour to make some cookies, she packed the remaining flour equally into 4 bags. What was the mass of flour in each bag?

A 6.1 kg

B 6.01 kg

C 6.49 kg

D 6.16 kg

7. 6 potted plants are arranged at equal distance from each other as shown below. What is the distance from the first to the last potted plant?

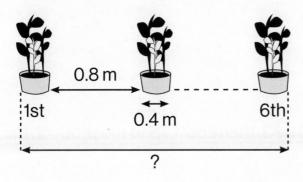

A 6.8 m

B 6 m

C 6.4 m

D 7.2 m

8. Raj has 5 coins in his wallet. They are either quarters or nickels. Which one of the following **cannot** be the amount of money in his wallet?

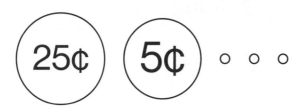

A $0.40

B $.045

C $0.65

D $0.85

9. Q is a number. Multiply Q by 3, then add 4.75 to the product, the answer is 20.05. What number is Q?

A 6.6

B 5.1

C 8.2

D 15.3

10. The poster below shows a chocolate sale in a grocery store.

Chocolate Sale

Buy 2 get 1 FREE

Regular Price: $7.05 per box

Edward wants to buy at least 8 boxes of chocolates for a party. What is the least amount of money he will have to pay?

A $21.15

B $56.40

C $28.20

D $42.30

Section B (2 points each)

11.   The sum of two numbers is 52.7. One number is 6.9 less than the other number.

       The smaller number is _____.

12.   The difference between the values of the digit 2 in 0.298 and 43.52

       is _____ .

13.   Emilia bought a 2-liter carton of orange juice. After she drank 0.45 L and her brother drank 0.6 L, how many liters of orange juice were left?

14. Gabe paid $15.35 for three of the following items. Check (✓) the three items he bought.

Book	Markers	(baseball)	(notebook with pencil)
A: $4.55	**B:** $5.35	**C:** $4.75	**D:** $5.45
☐	☐	☐	☐

15. Carmelo jogged 2.8 km on Saturday. On Sunday, he jogged $\frac{3}{4}$ km longer than on Saturday. What was the distance he jogged on Sunday? Give your answer in decimal form.

16. During a sale, oranges were sold at 5 for $3.80. How much did Anastasia pay for 20 oranges?

17. In a three-legged race, a 0.78-m long ribbon was used to tie the legs of 2 children together. What was the total length of ribbon needed if there were 18 children in the three-legged race?

18. The table below shows the mass of vegetables sold at a farmer's market in a day.

Vegetables	Amount sold (kg)
Tomatoes	61.2
Peppers	?
Onions	?
Total	204

If the mass of onions sold was twice the mass of peppers sold, how many kilograms of onions were sold?

19. A bowl of teriyaki is sold for $7. A restaurant sells 549 bowls of teriyaki in one day. How much money does the restaurant collect that day? Round your answer to the nearest $10.

```
┌─────────────────────────┐
│                         │
│                         │
│                         │
└─────────────────────────┘
```

20. A bag of popcorn costs $4.95. What is the greatest number of bags of popcorn Armond can buy with $20?

```
┌─────────────────────────┐
│                         │
│                         │
│                         │
└─────────────────────────┘
```

Section C (4 points each)

21. A roll of wire 10.1 m long is cut into two pieces. One piece is 4 times as long as the other piece. What is the length of the longer piece?

22. Sachleen had exactly enough money to buy 20 greeting cards. However, he bought 14 greeting cards and had $7.80 left. How much money did he have at first?

23. The total weight of 2 toy cars and 4 toy planes is 12.6 lb. The total weight of 1 toy car and 1 toy plane is 4.6 lb. What is the weight of each toy plane?

24. Nancy bought some fruit cups and smoothies for $23.80. A fruit cup and a smoothie cost $3 altogether. Each smoothie cost $1.40. She bought 2 more smoothies than fruit cups. How many smoothies did she buy?

25. 2 identical glasses and 3 identical bottles can hold a total of 4.16 L of water. Each bottle holds twice as much water as each glass. What is the capacity of each bottle?

Name: _____ Date: _____

Test A

60 min

70

Score

Continual Assessment 3

Section A (2 points each)
Circle the correct option: **A**, **B**, **C**, or **D**.

1. Which one of the following has the largest value?

    A 4.107   **B** 4.17

    C 4.017   **D** 4.1

2. Joshua's Great Dane has a mass of 49.8 kg
    when rounded to 1 decimal place.
    Which of the following could be the
    Great Dane's actual mass?

    A 49.08 kg   **B** 49.74 kg

    C 49.81 kg   **D** 49.86 kg

3. Express $90 + \dfrac{9}{100}$ as a decimal.

    A 90.9   **B** 90.09

    C 90.009   **D** 9.09

4. The sum of $3 + \dfrac{22}{100} + \dfrac{7}{10}$ is ___?___.

    A 3.722   **B** 3.227

    C 3.29   **D** 3.92

5. Which is the smallest number?

    A 0.99   **B** 1

    C 1.11   **D** 0.3

6. What number is 0.01 more than 157.4?

    A 157.5   **B** 158.4

    C 157.14   **D** 157.41

7. What is the value of n in $11.05 = 11 + \dfrac{5}{n}$?

    A 100   **B** 0.01

    C 10   **D** 0.1

8. What is the missing number?

$$\boxed{?} - 8.35 = 7.93$$

A 0.42

B 16.28

C 16.08

D 1.58

9. Which one of the following is equal to $\frac{3}{100}$ of $1?

A $3

B $0.30

C $0.03

D $10

10. What is 4 dollars and 3 dimes expressed as a fraction in its simplest form?

A $4\frac{3}{5}$ dollars

B $4\frac{3}{10}$ dollars

C $4\frac{3}{4}$ dollars

D $4\frac{3}{100}$ dollars

11.   Subtract 6 hundredths from 10 tenths. The answer is ___?___.

    A 0.94   **B** 0.60

    C 0.40   **D** 9.40

12.   The cost of 1 kg of apples is $2.60. Find the cost of 7 kg of apples.

    A $18.20   **B** $18.80

    C $20.80   **D** $19.80

13.   Sandrina saved the same amount of money each day. She saved
       $4.20 in a week. She saved ___?___ each day.

    A $0.70   **B** $4.20

    C $0.60   **D** $29.40

14. 8 stickers cost $1.50. What is the maximum number of stickers Maria can buy if she has $5?

    A 21   **B** 24

    C 27   **D** 32

15. Ryan bought 5 pens at $1.50 each. He gave the cashier $20. How much change did he receive?

    A $1.50   **B** $7.50

    C $12.50   **D** $18.50

Section B (2 points each)

16. In 3.975, the digit 7 is in the _____ place.

17. Arrange the decimals in order. Begin with the smallest.

_____, _____, _____, _____

18. Multiply.

$$
\begin{array}{r}
0.0\ 6 \\
\times\quad\ \ 4 \\
\hline
 \\
\hline
\end{array}
$$

19. Write 1 ten, 2 tenths, 3 hundredths, 4 thousandths as a decimal.

$$\boxed{}$$

20. What is 2 hundredths more than 8.99?

21. Write the missing number. Given that 10,800 + 3,300 = 14,100,

    then 10.8 + ☐ = 14.1.

22. Express 0.125 as a fraction in its simplest form.

    0.125 = _____

23. How many 0.1s are there in $3\frac{1}{2}$?

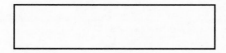

24. Find the value of 5 ÷ 7 to 1 decimal place.

25. Divide $0.75 by 3.

26. 1 m of pipe is sold at $10.45. Kelly needs to buy 7 m of pipe. What is the amount she has to pay? Round your answer to the nearest dollar.

27. In 58.397, the digit 5 stands for _____.

28. What is the value of X? Express your answer as a decimal.

29. The capacity of a pot is 1.58 qt. Round the capacity to one decimal place.

Section C (4 points each)

30. It takes 3.55 yd of fabric to make a tablecloth and 0.38 yd to make a napkin. Ethan wants to make a tablecloth and 6 napkins. How much fabric does he need?

31. Walter, Liliana, and Josef have a total of $33.20. Walter has $3 more than Liliana, while Liliana has $4 more than Josef. How much money does Walter have?

32. Jung-soon had just enough money to buy 8 hair clips. If she only bought 3 hair clips, she would have $8.75 left. How much money did she have before buying any hair clips?

Extra Credit

1. Supriya's mom gave her some money to buy magazines. If Supriya buys 7 magazines, she will be short $1.50. If she buys 5 magazines, she will have $3.50 extra. How much does each magazine cost?

2. In a shop, a pen is sold for $0.70. A package of 2 such pens is sold for $1.10. A package of 3 such pens is sold for $1.50. If the pattern continues, what is the cost of a package of 6 pens?

BLANK

Name: _____ Date: _____

Test B

60 min

Continual Assessment 3

Section A (2 points each)
Circle the correct option: **A**, **B**, **C**, or **D**.

1. In 37.085, the digit ___?___ is in the thousandths place.

   A 3

   B 5

   C 8

   D 7

2. 4 ones 5 thousandths is the same as ___?___.

   A 5,004

   B 4.05

   C 0.405

   D 4.005

3. 0.75 is the same as ___?___.

   A $\frac{2}{3}$ **B** $\frac{5}{8}$ **C** $\frac{3}{4}$ **D** $\frac{1}{2}$

4. The length of a piece of wire is 29.8 m when rounded to 1 decimal place. Which option below could be its actual length?

   A 29.08 m   **B** 29.84 m

   C 29.74 m   **D** 29.86 m

5. The best estimate for the length of this pencil to the nearest centimeter is ___?___ .

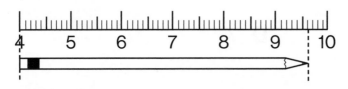

   A 5.6 cm   **B** 6 cm

   C 9.6 cm   **D** 10 cm

6. What is the sum of 14 tens and 14 tenths?

   A 14.14   **B** 15.4

   C 140.14   **D** 141.4

7. Which one of the following is equal to $\frac{3}{20}$?

    A 3.2   **B** 0.3

    C 0.15   **D** 0.12

8. Which one of the following has the largest value?

    A 0.25   **B** $\frac{1}{4}$

    C 2 tenths 2 hundredths   **D** 0.1 + 0.16

9. What is the sum of 3 dollars 15 cents and 7 dollars 7 cents expressed as a decimal?

    A $10.85   **B** $10.22

    C $3.22   **D** $7.85

10. The mass of 30 apples is 4.5 kg. What is the mass of 4 apples?

    A 60 g   **B** 0.6 kg

    C 1.5 g   **D** 6 g

11. The figure shows the time counting down on an egg timer. The egg timer shows ___?___ time left.

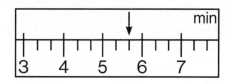

A 5.6 min

B 6.2 min

C 6 min 20 s

D 5 min 40 s

12. The following shows the price of apples and oranges. How much does it cost to buy 3 apples and 4 oranges?

Price of one apple	$0.65
Price of one orange	$0.50

A $1.95

B $2.00

C $1.05

D $3.95

13. The product of two numbers is 250. If one of the numbers is 2.5, the sum of the two numbers is ___?___.

A 2.5

B 102.5

C 1,002.5

D 100

14. What is the missing number?

$$\frac{1}{8} + \frac{1}{8} + \frac{1}{8} + \frac{1}{8} = \boxed{} \times 0.25$$

A 1

B 2

C 3

D 4

15. The total length of two pieces of wire is 24 m. The longer piece is 2.4 m longer than the shorter piece. The length of the longer piece of wire is ___?___.

A 10.8 m

B 12.2 m

C 13.2 m

D 14.2 m

Section B (2 points each)

16. What is the missing number?

$$4.126 = 4 + \boxed{} + 0.006$$

17. How many hundredths make 9.15?

$$\boxed{}$$

18. What is the missing number?

$$35.626 = 35 + \frac{62}{100} + \frac{\boxed{}}{1,000}$$

19. Divide. Round the answer to 2 decimal places.

$$27.3 \div 4$$

$$\boxed{}$$

20. _____ is 8 hundredths less than 5.6.

21. Write 1 one, 8 hundredths, 5 thousandths as a decimal.

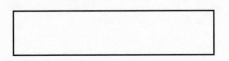

22. Arrange the numbers in decreasing order.

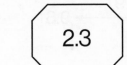 2.3 $3\frac{3}{4}$ $2\frac{5}{10}$ 3.7

_____, _____, _____, _____

23. Complete the number pattern.

97.684, 97.68, _____, 97.672, _____, _____

24. What number does the letter X represent below?
Express your answer as a decimal.

3   X   7

```
┌─────────────────┐
│                 │
│                 │
└─────────────────┘
```

25. 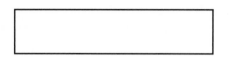 stands for a number. Multiply the number by 6, then add 3.97 to the product. The answer is 9.31.

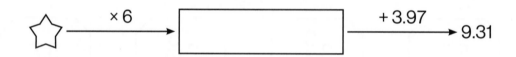

☆ stands for _____ .

26. Below is a series of numbers from 12.9 to 15.6 with a 0.3 increase in each number.

12.9, 13.2, 13.5, 13.8, ... , 15.6

How many numbers are missing from the series?

```
┌─────────────────┐
│                 │
│                 │
└─────────────────┘
```

27. Melody mixed $1\frac{1}{4}$ liters of dye mix with 7.2 liters of water for an art project. How many liters of dye did she make? Give your answer in decimal form.

28. A piece of wire 21.8 m long is cut into 2 pieces. One piece is 3.6 m longer than the other piece. Find the length of the longer piece.

29. The cost of 3 books and 1 magazine is $30. The cost of 1 book and 1 magazine is $15.80. What is the cost of the magazine?

Section C (4 points each)

30. A roll of 100 stamps cost $47. A sheet of 10 stamps costs $4.70. Fadiya bought 1 roll and 5 sheets of stamps. She gave the postal clerk $80. How much change did she receive?

31. Alex sealed 2 small and 5 large packages with packing tape. Each small package needed 1.52 yd of tape and each large package needed 2.75 yd of tape. Alex started with a roll of tape 50 yd long. How many yards of tape were left when he finished?

32. Akiko paid $31.50 for 3 board games and 2 card games. Each card game was $1.50 cheaper than each board game. What was the cost of a board game?

Extra Credit

1. 5 pineapples and 3 watermelons cost $35.75. 7 pineapples and 6 watermelons cost $55.90. How much more does a pineapple cost than a watermelon?

2. Wendi paid a total of $22.60 for 4 holiday cards and 3 birthday cards. Each holiday card cost $1.80 more than each birthday card. What was the cost of each birthday card?

Name: _____ Date: _____

Test A 25 min

Unit 8 – Part 1 Geometry

60
Score

Section A (2 points each)
Circle the correct option: **A**, **B**, **C**, or **D**.

1. Which of the following describes this diagram?

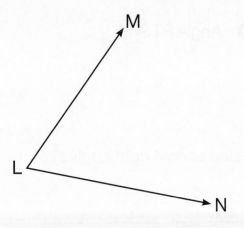

A Two lines LM and LN intersect at L

B Line segments LM and LN form an angle at point L

C Two rays LM and LN form an angle at point L

D Three points L, M, and N

2. Which of the following is not an angle formed by the intersecton of line PQ and line RS?

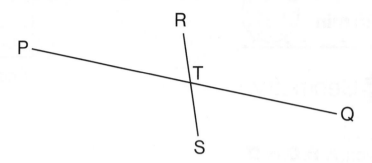

A Angle PRS   **B** Angle RTQ

C Angle STQ   **D** Angle PTS

3. Which figure below has 4 equal sides and 4 right angles?

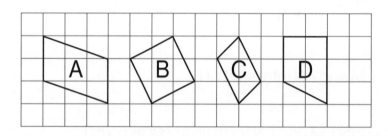

A A   **B** B

C C   **D** D

4. ABCD is a rectangle. What is m ∠ADE?

A 24°

B 34°

C 44°

D 90°

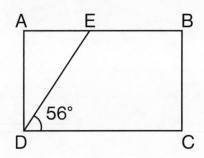

5. Which of the following is equal to $\frac{3}{4}$ of a complete turn?

A 90°

B 180°

C 270°

D 360°

6. Which of the following is an obtuse angle?

A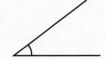

B

C

D A

7.   Which of the following angles has a measure of 125°?

A

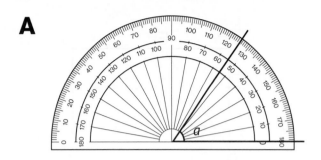

B

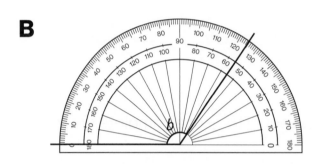

C

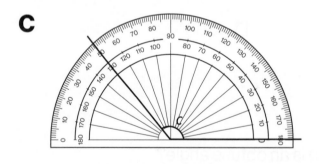

D

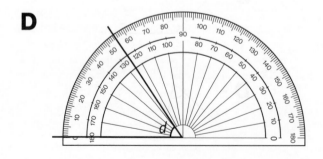

Study the diagram. Answer questions 8 to 10.

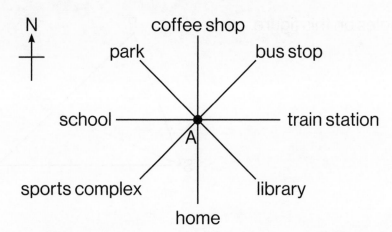

8.   Alberto is at point A facing the park. If he turns 1 right angle in a clockwise direction, where will he be facing?

A bus stop   **B** train station

C library   **D** coffee shop

9.   Jaya is at point A facing the school. If she makes a $\frac{1}{4}$-turn in a counterclockwise direction, where will she be facing?

A home   **B** train station

C coffee shop   **D** library

10. Seth is at point A facing the sports complex. How many degrees must he turn in a clockwise direction to face the library?

A 90°   **B** 135°

C 225°   **D** 270°

11. Label the angles on this figure.
    ∠PSQ as *e*
    ∠PQS as *f*
    ∠SQR as *g*
    ∠QRS as *h*

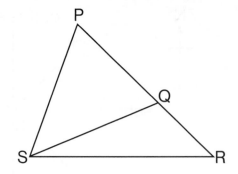

12. Shade the figures that are rectangles.

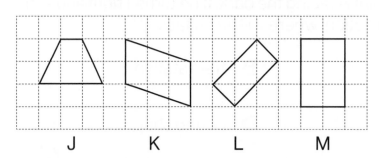

     J   K   L   M

13. Complete the table below. Check (✔) the correct boxes.

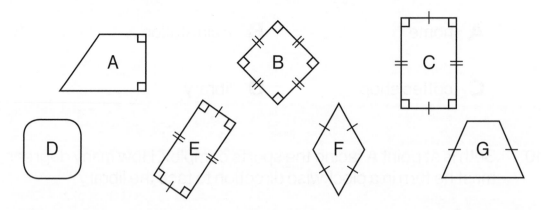

Figures	A	B	C	D	E	F	G
Is it a square?							
Is it a rectangle?							

14. Mark all the right angles in this figure.

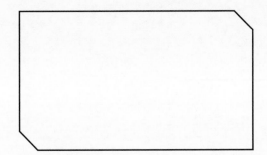

15. Find the unknown marked angle in this rectangle.

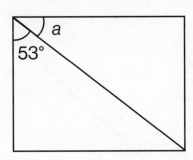

m ∠a = _____

16. STUV is a rectangle where m ∠STV = m ∠TVU. Find m ∠x.

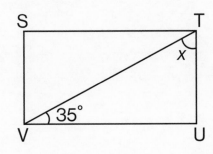

m ∠x = _____

17. Find the unknown angle.

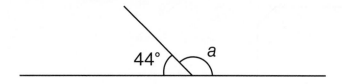

m ∠a = _____

18. Study the figure to the right.

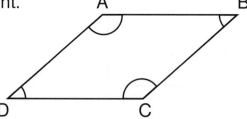

a) Name the obtuse angles.

_____

b) Name the acute angles.

_____

19. Arrange the angles inside the triangle below in order. Begin with the greatest.

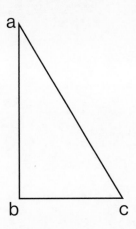

_____, _____, _____
greatest   smallest

20. Measure and write the size of ∠y.

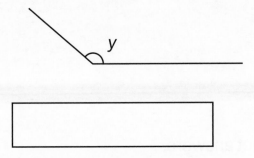

21. Circle the angle strip that shows an angle between 180° and 270°.

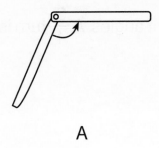

A

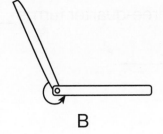

B

22. Complete the drawing of ∠ABC = 70° using the line AB below.

B ├———————————————— A

23. Draw ∠a = 40° using the given vertex and ray.

•————————————————→

24. Fill in the blanks with the correct answers.

(a) A quarter turn is _____ right angle(s). A $\frac{1}{4}$-turn is _____°.

(b) A half turn is _____ right angles. A $\frac{1}{2}$-turn is _____°.

(c) A three-quarter turn is _____ right angles. A $\frac{3}{4}$-turn is

_____°.

25. Grace is facing east. If she turns 180° in a counterclockwise direction, which direction will she be facing?

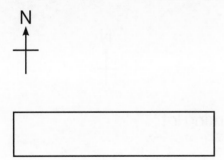

26. Jeremy is facing west. If he makes a $\frac{3}{4}$-turn in a clockwise direction, which direction will he be facing?

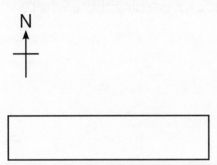

27. Look at the clocks below. How many right angles has the minute hand moved?

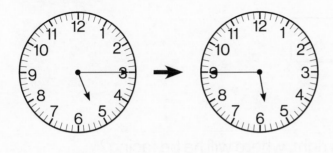

Desmond is standing at point M, facing the fish pond. Study the diagram and answer questions 28 to 30.

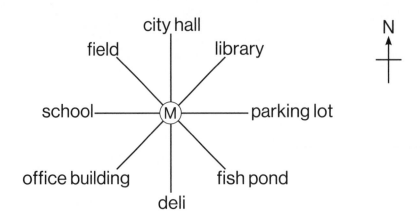

28. If he makes a $\frac{1}{2}$-turn in a counterclockwise direction, where will he be facing?

29. How many degrees must he turn in a counterclockwise direction to face city hall?

30. If he turns 270° to his right, where will he be facing?

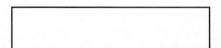

Name: _____ Date: _____

Test B

25 min

☐
60
Score

Unit 8 – Part 1 Geometry

Section A (2 points each)
Circle the correct option: **A**, **B**, **C**, or **D**.

1.　A ___?___ is part of a line between two points.

　　A ray　　　　　　　**B** line segment

　　C point　　　　　　**D** angle

2.　Which of the following lists all the line segments in Figure Y?

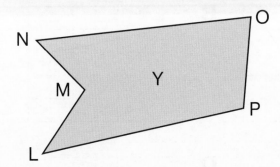

　　A LM, LN, LP, LO　　　**B** LM, MN, NO, OP, LO

　　C LM, MN, NO, OP　　　**D** LM, MN, NO, OP, PL

3. Which of the following does not have at least one right angle?

A 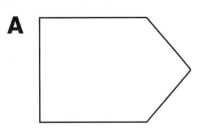   B

C 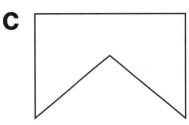   D

4. Which figure has no acute angle?

A    B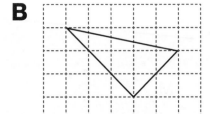

C 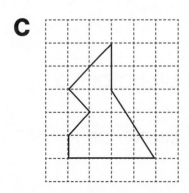   D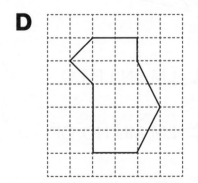

5. In the figure below, ABCD is a rectangle. Find m ∠a.

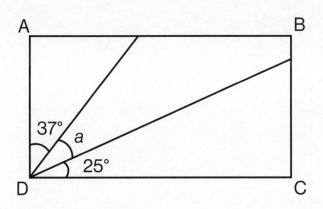

A 25°   **B** 28°   **C** 37°   **D** 62°

6. In the figure below, what is the measure of ∠a?

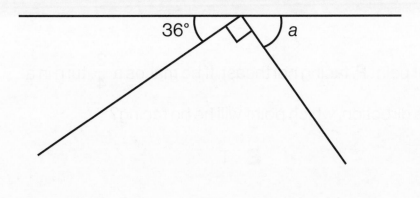

A 54°   **B** 154°   **C** 144°   **D** 126°

Use the diagram below to answer questions 7 and 8.

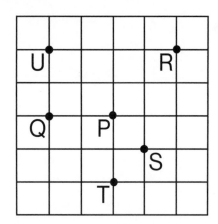

7. Isabella is at point P, facing west. If she turns 135° in a counterclockwise direction, which point will she be facing?

    A T   **B** Q

    C R   **D** S

8. Frank is at point P, facing northeast. If he makes a $\frac{3}{4}$-turn in a clockwise direction, which point will he be facing?

    A U   **B** T

    C S   **D** R

The table below consists of letters from A to P. Use the table to answer questions 9 and 10.

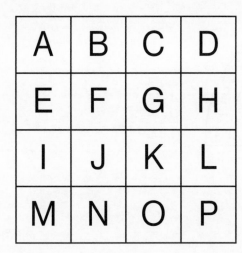

9. Which letter is west of P and also south of B?

A F

B J

C M

D N

10. Which letter is southeast of F and north of O?

A K

B O

C C

D E

Section B (2 points each)

11.   What is the measure of ∠x?

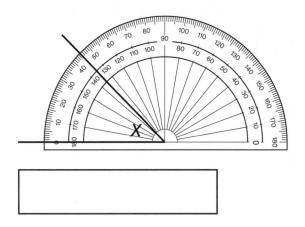

12.   Label the angles in this figure.

∠UWV as w
∠TUW as x
∠UOV as y
∠TOU as z

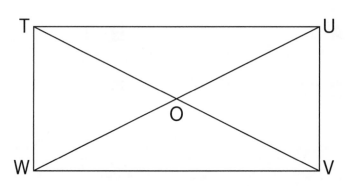

13.   Which one of the following angles measures between 110° and 130°?
      Circle it.

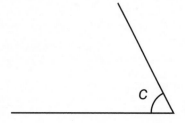
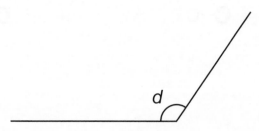

Study the figures below. Answer questions 14 to 16.

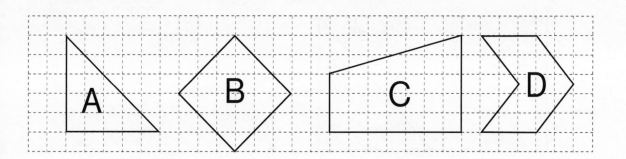

14. Which three figures have at least 1 right angle?

15. Which two figures have at least 1 obtuse angle?

16. Which three figures have at least 1 acute angle?

17. Find the unknown marked angle in this rectangle.

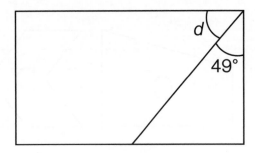

   m ∠d = _____

18. Find the unknown angle.

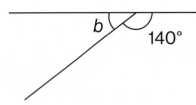

   m ∠b = _____

19. Join point C with either point A or B to form a 100 degree angle.

   A•   •B

   •————————————————
   C

20. Use a protractor to measure the marked angle.

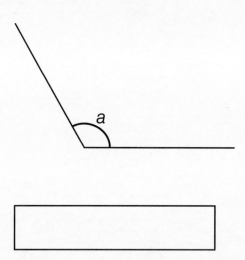

```
┌─────────────────────────────┐
│                             │
│                             │
│                             │
└─────────────────────────────┘
```

21. Use a protractor to measure ∠ABC.

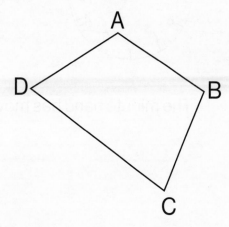

```
┌─────────────────────────────┐
│                             │
│                             │
│                             │
└─────────────────────────────┘
```

22. Draw ∠POQ = 130°. Mark and label the angle.

23. Look at the clocks below.

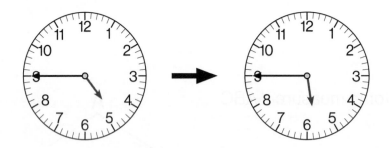

The minute hand has moved _____ right angles.

24. Jeremy is facing northwest. Which direction will he be facing if he makes a $\frac{1}{4}$-turn in a counterclockwise direction?

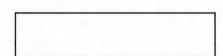

25. Fill in the blanks with the correct answers.

a) A quarter turn is _____ right angle(s). A $\frac{1}{4}$-turn is

_____°.

b) A complete turn is _____ right angles. It is _____°.

c) _____ of a complete turn is 90°.

26. The figure below shows an arrow that spins. It makes a $\frac{3}{4}$-turn in a

counterclockwise direction. Draw the final position of the arrow on

the grid.

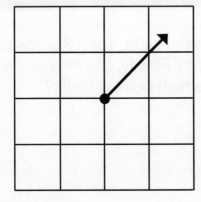

Study the diagram below and answer questions 27 and 28.

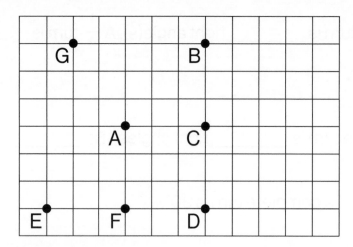

27.   Jayden is at a point which is northwest of point D and southwest of point B. At which point is Jayden?

28.   Lily is at point D. She moves 3 steps to the west. Then 3 steps to the north followed by 3 steps to the east. Finally, she moves 3 steps to the north to meet up with Malik. At which point is Malik?

29. It is 6:45 p.m. now. What time will it be if the minute hand turns 3 right angles in a clockwise direction?

30. Mark is at point R. If he turns 135° in a clockwise direction, then makes a $\frac{1}{4}$-turn in a counterclockwise direction, he will be facing the library. Which place is he facing now?

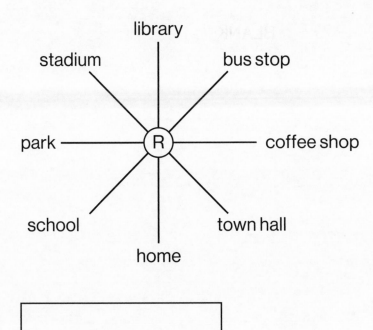

BLANK

Name: _____ Date: _____

Test A

25 min

60

Score

Unit 8 – Part 2 Geometry

Section A (2 points each)
Circle the correct option: **A**, **B**, **C**, or **D**.

1. Which line is perpendicular to line EF?

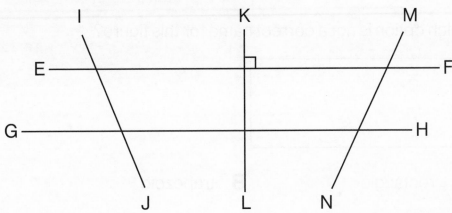

A GH   **B** IJ   **C** KL   **D** MN

2. Which pair of lines is parallel?

A

B

C

D

3. Which of the following does not have any perpendicular lines?

A   **B**

C 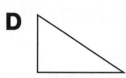   **D**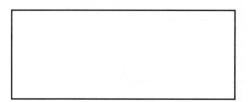

4. Which option is not a correct name for this figure?

A rectangle   **B** trapezoid

C parallelogram   **D** square

5. The figure below is made up of a rectangle and a square. What is the length of AD?

A 9 cm

B 12 cm

C 14 cm

D 15 cm

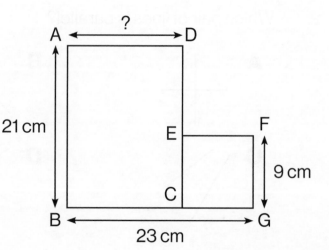

6. How many equal sides does an equilateral triangle have?

    A 1   **B** 2

    C 3   **D** none

7. Which one of the following is a symmetric figure?

    A 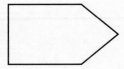   **B**

    C 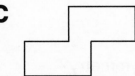   **D**

8. Which one of the following is not a symmetric figure?

    A    **B**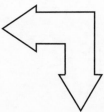

    C 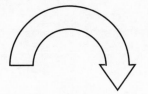   **D**

9. Which of the following letters is not symmetric?

A

B

C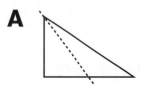

D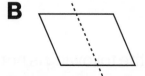

10. In which figure is the dotted line a line of symmetry?

A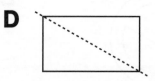

Section B (2 points each)

11. Check (✔) the box if the lines are parallel.

a)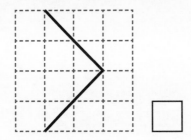

☐

b)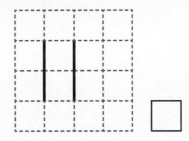

☐

12. Draw a line that is parallel to line MN and passes through point P.

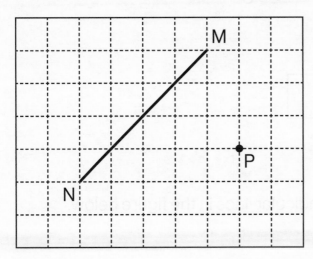

13. Which point (C, D, or E), when joined to point M, can form a line that is perpendicular to line AB?

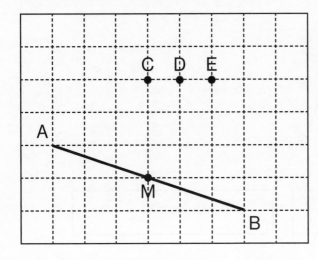

Answer: _____

14. Name a pair of parallel lines in the figure below.

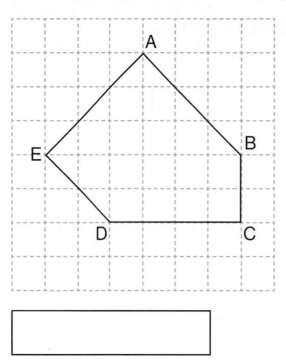

15. Name 2 pairs of perpendicular lines in the figure below.

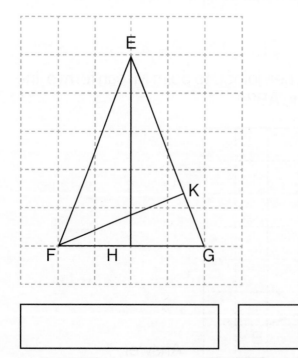

16. Which of these polygons are quadrilaterals?

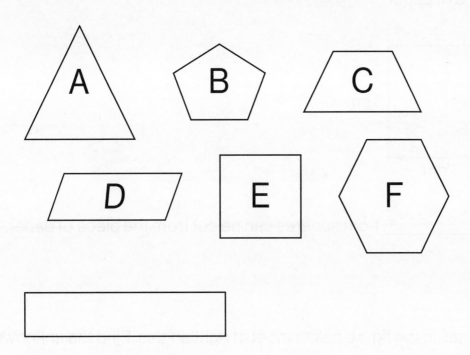

17. Use a straight line to divide each of the figures below into a square and a rectangle.

a)
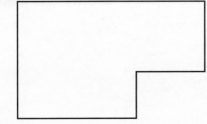

b)
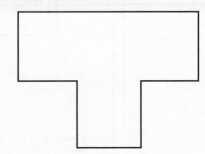

c)
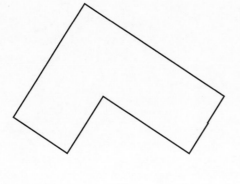

d)
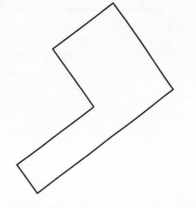

18. Draw lines to show how 1-cm squares can be cut from the following piece of paper.

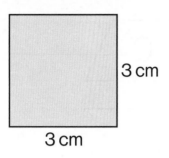

3 cm

3 cm

_____ 1-cm squares can be cut from the piece of paper.

19. All lines in the figure below meet at right angles. Find the unknown length.

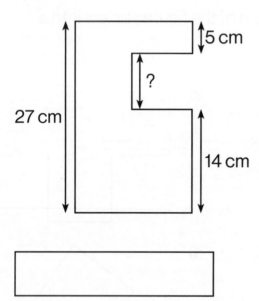

5 cm

?

27 cm

14 cm

20. The figure below is made up of two squares. Find the two unknown lengths DE and BG.

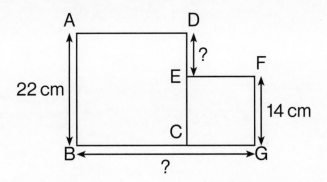

DE = _____

BG = _____

21. All lines in this figure meet at right angles. Find the unknown marked length.

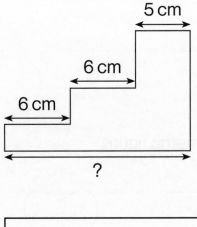

```
┌──────────────────────────────────┐
│                                  │
└──────────────────────────────────┘
```

22. Look at the figure below.

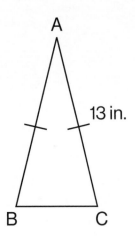

13 in.

AB = _____

23. Label each triangle below as **Isosceles**, **Scalene**, or **Equilateral**.

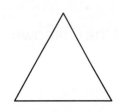  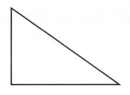

_____ _____ _____

24. Circle the shape below that is a symmetric figure.

25. Circle the letter below that is a symmetric figure.

26. Circle the figure below in which the dotted line is a line of symmetry.

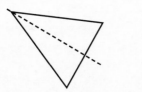 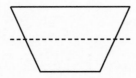 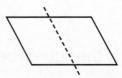

27. Draw a line of symmetry for the figure below.

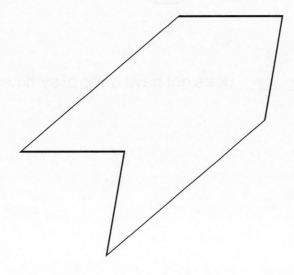

28. Draw a line of symmetry for the figure below.

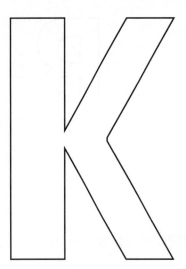

29. Study the figures below.

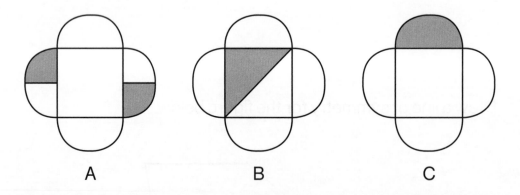

A   B   C

Figure _____ does not have a line of symmetry.

30. Complete each of the symmetric figures below using the dotted line as a line of symmetry.

a)

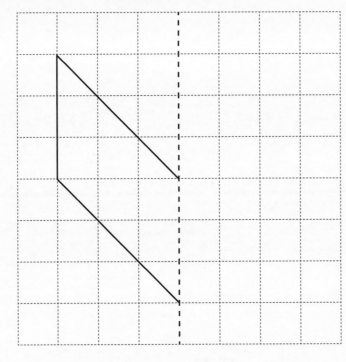

b)

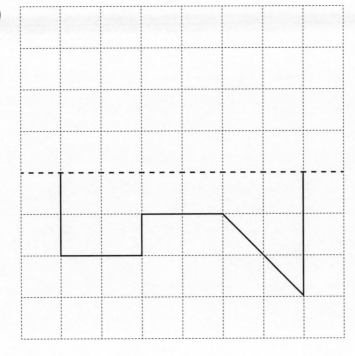

BLANK

Name: _____ Date: _____

Test B

25 min

60

Score

Unit 8 – Part 2 Geometry

Section A (2 points each)
Circle the correct option: **A**, **B**, **C**, or **D**.

1. Which of the following figures have at least 2 pairs of parallel lines?

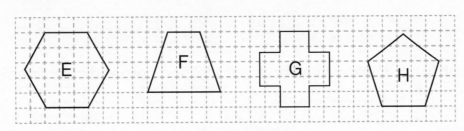

  A E only

  B G only

  C E and H

  D E and G

2. How many pairs of perpendicular lines are there in the figure below?

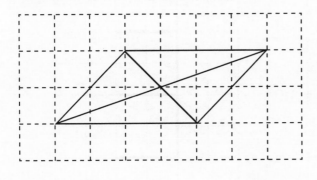

  A 1

  B 2

  C 3

  D 0

3. In the figure below, which line is parallel to line DE?

A AB

B CF

C AE

D CG

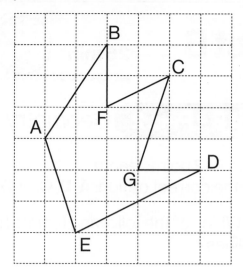

4. Which letters below have both parallel and perpendicular lines?

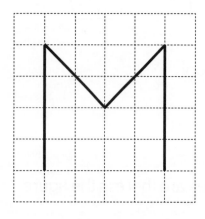

A M only   **B** E only   **C** M and E   **D** M, K, and E

5. Which of these figures is not a parallelogram?

A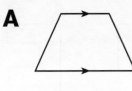
Figure A

B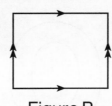
Figure B

C
Figure C

D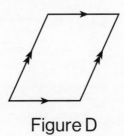
Figure D

6. How many lines of symmetry are there in this figure?

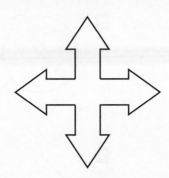

A 6

B 2

C 8

D 4

7. How many letters below have exactly 1 line of symmetry?

 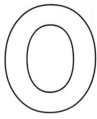  

A 1

B 2

C 3

D 4

8. Which figure below has exactly 2 lines of symmetry?

A

B

C

D

9.   Which figure below does not have a line of symmetry?

A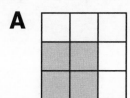

B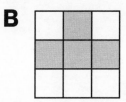

C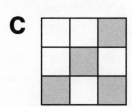

D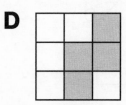

10.   Which square must be shaded so that the figure below has a line
      of symmetry?

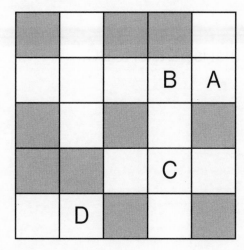

A A

B B

C C

D D

Section B (2 points each)

11. In the figure below, which line is parallel to AB and perpendicular to BC?

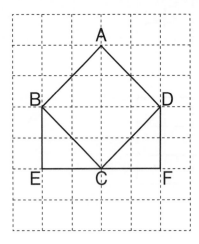

12. In the grid below, draw a line AD that is parallel to BC.

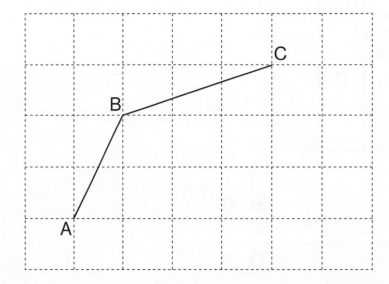

13. Study the figures below.

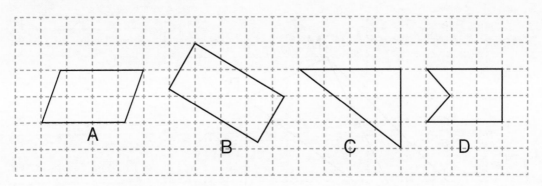

a) Which figures have at least one pair of perpendicular lines?

b) Which figures have at least one pair of parallel lines?

c) Which figures have both perpendicular and parallel lines?

14. Name three pairs of perpendicular lines in the figure below.

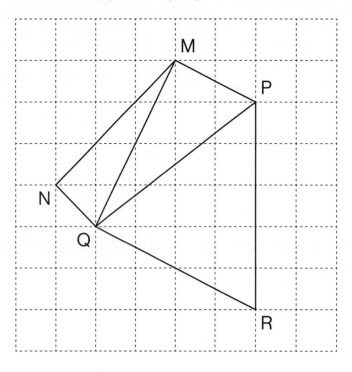

15. Circle True or False.

a) A polygon is a closed figure with straight lines.　　　　　True　　　False

b) A parallelogram is always a rhombus.　　　　　True　　　False

c) A parallelogram is both a trapezoid and a quadrilateral.　　　　　True　　　False

d) A square can be called a rhombus or a rectangle.　　　　　True　　　False

16. Draw straight lines to divide each figure below into 3 rectangles. Each figure should be divided in a different way.

First way

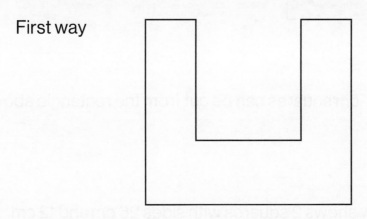

Second way

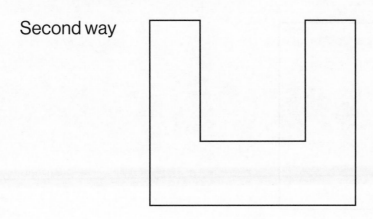

Third way

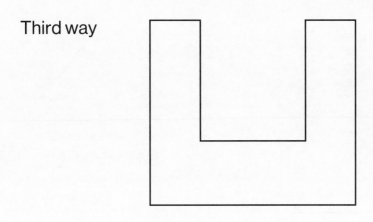

17.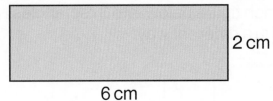

2 cm

6 cm

_____ 1-cm squares can be cut from the rectangle above.

18. The figure below shows 2 squares with sides 26 cm and 12 cm respectively. Find the unknown length.

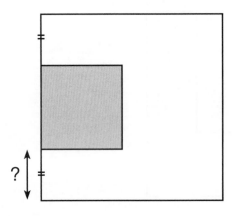

?

19. A rectangular card was folded to form the shape as shown below. What was the length of the rectangular card before it was folded?

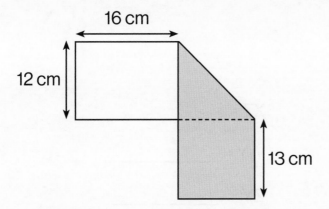

16 cm

12 cm

13 cm

20. Look at the figure below and fill in the blanks.

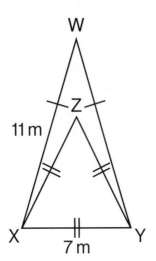

XZ = _____

WY = _____

ZY = _____

21. Figure ABC is an equilateral triangle. The distance around Figure ABC is 54 ft.

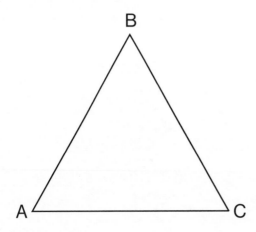

BC = _____

22. Check (✓) the box for each figure for which the dotted line is a line of symmetry.

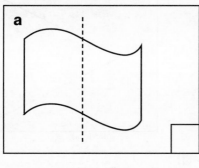

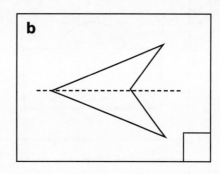

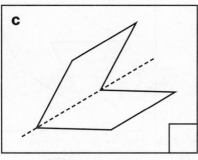

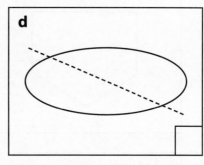

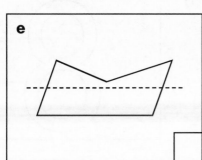

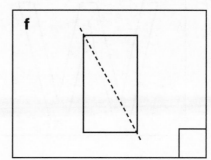

23. How many lines of symmetry are there in this rectangle?

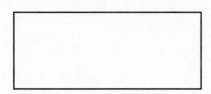

Answer: _____

24. Draw a line of symmetry on each figure below.

a)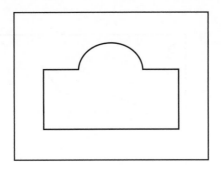

b)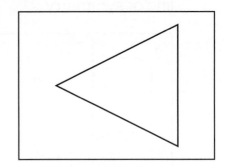

c)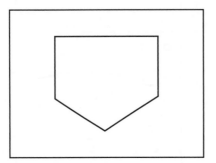

d)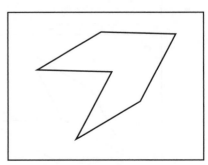

e)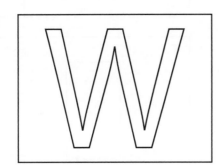

f)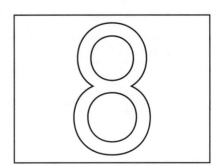

25. How many lines of symmetry are there in the figure below?

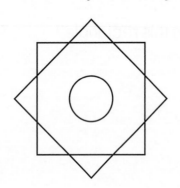

Answer: _____

26. Study the figures below.

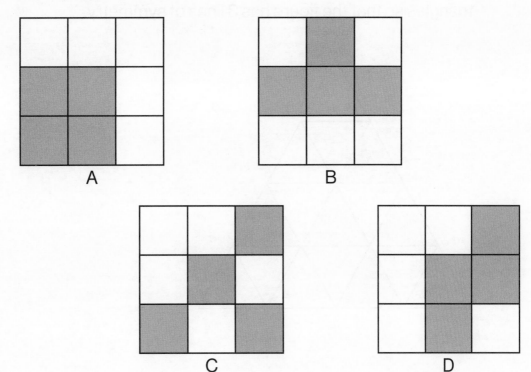

A

B

C

D

Figure _____ does not have a line of symmetry.

27. Complete the symmetric figure below using the dotted line as the line of symmetry.

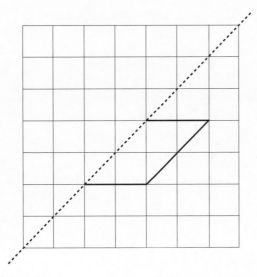

28. The figure below is made up of equilateral triangles. Shade 2 more triangles so that the figure has 3 lines of symmetry.

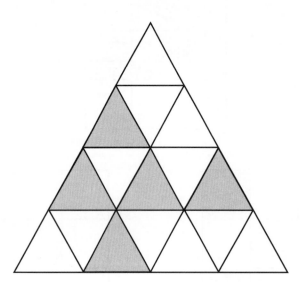

29. Shade one more square in the figure below to make it symmetric.

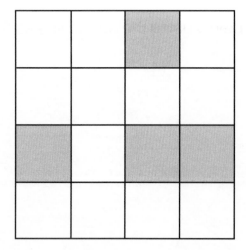

30. Complete each of the symmetric figures below using the dotted line as a line of symmetry.

a)

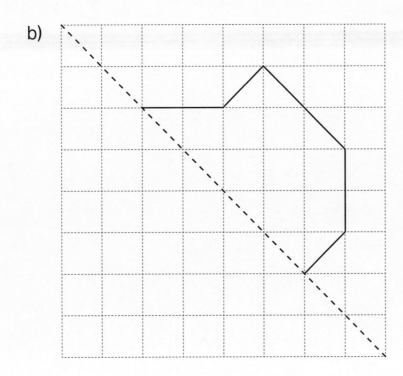

b)

BLANK

Name: _____   Date: _____

Test A   **30 min**

45

Score

Unit 9 Area and Perimeter

Section A (2 points each)
Circle the correct option: **A**, **B**, **C**, or **D**.

1. The perimeter of a square is 64 cm. What is the length of the
    square?

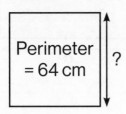

Perimeter
= 64 cm
?

A 8 cm   **B** 16 cm

C 32 cm   **D** 40 cm

2. The perimeter of a rectangle is 100 cm. Given that the length of
    the rectangle is 30 cm, what is the width of the rectangle?

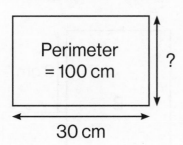

Perimeter
= 100 cm
?

30 cm

A 20 cm   **B** 35 cm

C 40 cm   **D** 70 cm

3. The area of a square is 81 m². What is the perimeter of this square?

A 9 m

B 18 m

C 36 m

D 162 m

4. The area of a rectangle is 48 cm².
Given that its length is 2 cm longer
than its width, what is its length?

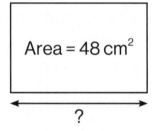

A 6 cm

B 8 cm

C 12 cm

D 24 cm

5. The figure below is made up of square A and rectangle B. If the
width of rectangle B is 7 cm, what is its length?

A 12 cm

B 9 cm

C 14 cm

D 16 cm

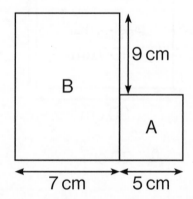

Section B (2 points each)

6. The perimeter of a rectangle is 36 m. If the width of the rectangle is 8 m, what is its length?

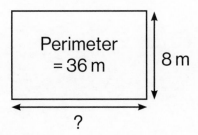

Answer:

7. Given that the perimeter of a square is 48 cm, what is its area?

Perimeter
= 48 cm

Answer:

8. The area of a rectangular field is 28 m². If the width of the field is 4 m, what is its perimeter?

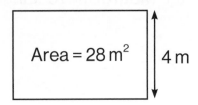

Answer:

9. The figure below shows square WXYZ. What is the area of the shaded part?

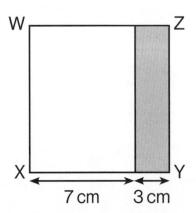

Answer:

10. Square C has the same area as rectangle D. What is the length of rectangle D?

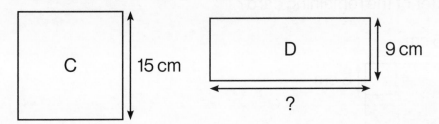

Answer: _____

11. Square A has the same perimeter as rectangle B. What is the length of square A?

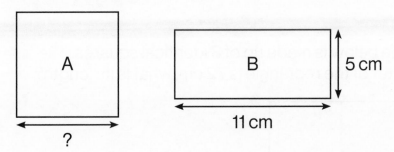

Answer: _____

12. A small square with 3-cm sides is cut out from each corner of a square card with 15-cm sides as shown below. What is the perimeter of the remaining card?

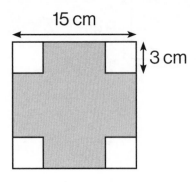

15 cm

3 cm

Answer:

13. The rectangle below is made up of 3 identical squares. If the perimeter of the rectangle is 72 cm, what is its length?

Answer:

14. A square piece of paper with a perimeter of 72 cm is folded in half as shown below. What is the area of the new Figure B?

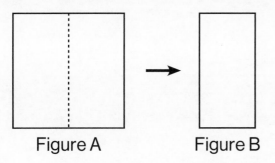

Figure A   Figure B

Answer:

15. A square carpet is cut equally into 4 smaller square rugs. The area of each square rug is 16 m². What was the perimeter of the carpet at first?

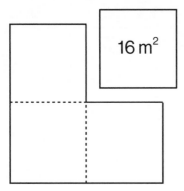

16 m²

Answer:

Section C (5 points each)

16. A rectangle is painted on the roof of an apartment building measuring 19 m by 16 m. A margin 2 m wide is left unpainted around the rectangle as shown below. What is the area that was painted?

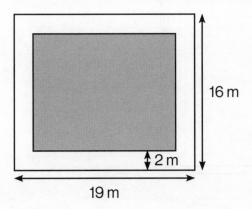

17. A rectangular classroom measures 20 m by 15 m. A carpet is placed on the floor of the room, leaving space around it. What is the area of the floor not covered by the carpet?

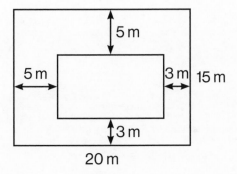

18. A path 1 m wide is built around a rectangular plot of land measuring 32 m by 18 m. What is the area of the path?

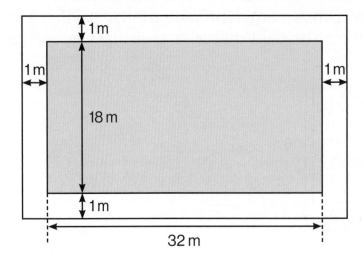

Name: _____   Date: _____

Test B  **30 min**

45

Score

Unit 9 Area and Perimeter

Section A (2 points each)
Circle the correct option: **A**, **B**, **C**, or **D**.

1. The figure below is made up of rectangle ABCD and square
    BEFC. If the area of the square is 49 cm^2, what is the area of
    rectangle AEFD?

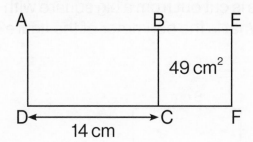

A   A 56 cm^2 **B** 98 cm^2

C 147 cm^2 **D** 196 cm^2

2. The figure below is made up of a rectangle and a square.
    What is the perimeter of the figure?

A 17 cm

B 34 cm

C 37 cm

D 44 cm

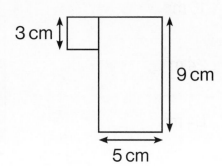

3. The figure below is made up of 2 different rectangles. What is the
    area of the figure?

    A 104 m²

    B 128 m²

    C 168 m²

    D 184 m²

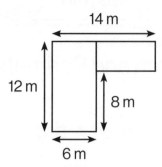

4. A small square with 5-cm sides is cut out from a big square with
    8-cm sides as shown below. What is the perimeter of the figure?

    A 47 cm

    B 34 cm

    C 39 cm

    D 42 cm

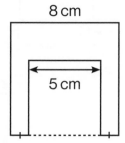

5. A sidewalk 1 m wide was built around a rectangular garden as
    shown below. What is the area of the garden?

    A 16 m²

    B 24 m²

    C 64 m²

    D 80 m²

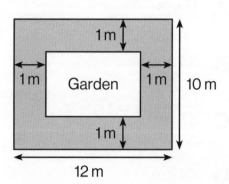

Section B (2 points each)

6. All lines in the figure below meet at right angles. What is the perimeter of the figure?

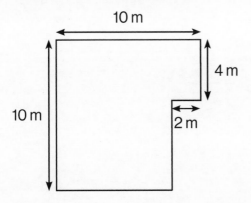

Answer:

7. All lines in the figure below meet at right angles. What is the area of the figure?

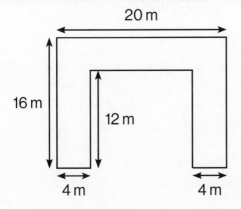

Answer:

8.   Find the area of the shaded figure in the diagram below.

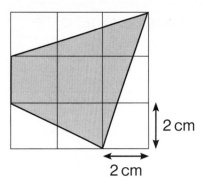

2 cm

2 cm

Answer:

9.   The length of a rectangular garden is twice its width. It is divided
      into 4 equal parts as shown below. Given that the area of each part
      is 32 m^2, what is the length of the rectangular garden?

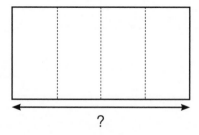

?

Answer:

10. The figure below shows 2 identical pieces of rectangular paper overlapping each other. Find the perimeter of the figure.

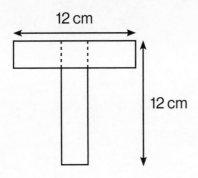

12 cm

12 cm

Answer:

11. A rectangular field measures 16 m by 10 m. It is surrounded by a 2-m wide path as shown below. What is the total area of the path?

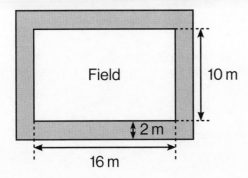

Field

10 m

2 m

16 m

Answer:

12. In the figure below, the area of square A is 9 m². The area of square C is 49 m². Find the area of the figure.

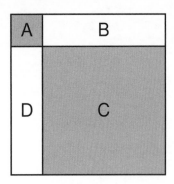

Answer:

13. The figure below is formed by 3 identical squares with sides of 20 cm overlapping one another. All angles in the figure are right angles.Find the area of the figure.

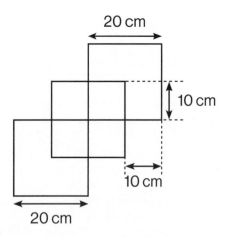

20 cm

10 cm

10 cm

20 cm

Answer:

14. The figure below is made up of 2 identical rectangles partially overlapping each other. All angles in the figure are right angles. Find the perimeter of the figure.

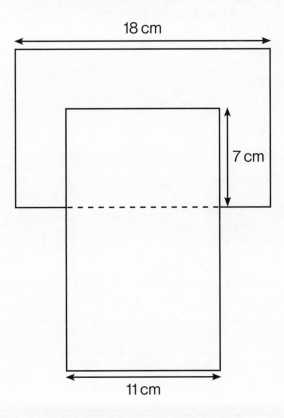

18 cm

7 cm

11 cm

Answer: _____

15. A rectangular strip of paper is folded as shown below. What is the area of the strip of paper before it was folded?

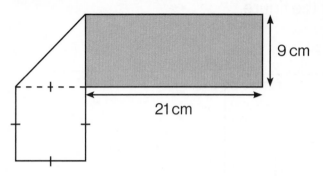

9 cm

21 cm

Answer: [   ]

Section C (5 points each)

16. A rectangular paper measures 14 cm by 11 cm. A rectangular photograph is pasted on it, leaving a border 2 cm wide all around it. What is the area of the border?

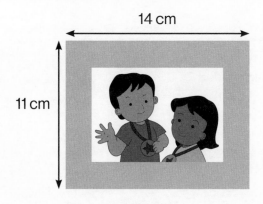

17. Laila wants to walk a total of 800 yd around a field measuring 55 yd by 25 yd. How many times does she have to walk around the field?

18. Brynn has a piece of cardboard measuring 24 cm by 18 cm. She cut out a square with 10-cm sides from the center, cut the remaining piece in half, and then joined the 2 equal halves together as shown below.

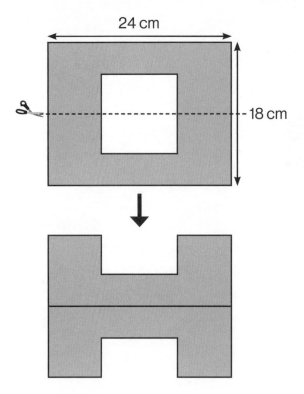

Find:

a) the perimeter of the remaining cardboard.

b) the area of the remaining cardboard.

Name: _____ Date: _____

Test A

20 min

Unit 10 Bar Graphs and Line Plots

Section A (2 points each)
Circle the correct option: **A**, **B**, **C**, or **D**.

The line plot below shows the number of pairs of women's shoes by size sold at a store last Monday.

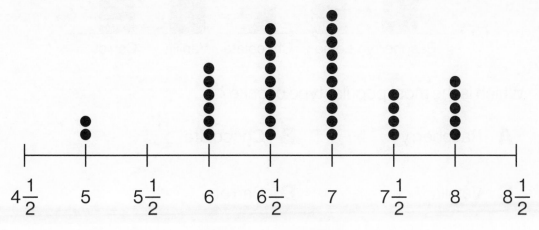

Size of women's shoes

1. How many pairs of women's shoes were sold?

    A 33   **B** 30   **C** 35   **D** 36

2. What is the most common size of women's shoes sold?

    A $6\frac{1}{2}$ **B** 7   **C** $5\frac{1}{2}$ **D** 8

The graph below shows a bakery's sales of different types of cakes in a day. Use it to answer questions 3 to 5.

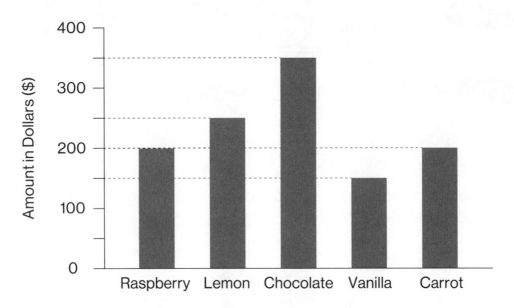

3. Which is the most popular type of cake?

   A Raspberry   **B** Chocolate

   C Vanilla   **D** Carrot

4. What is the difference in sales between the most popular and the least popular type of cake?

   A $100   **B** $150

   C $200   **D** $350

5. What was the total amount collected from the sale of cakes on this day?

   A $1,150   **B** $1,050

   C $1,100   **D** $1,200

Section B (2 points each)

The bar graph below shows the number of books sold at a bookstore over a week. Answer questions 6 to 10 on this page and the following page.

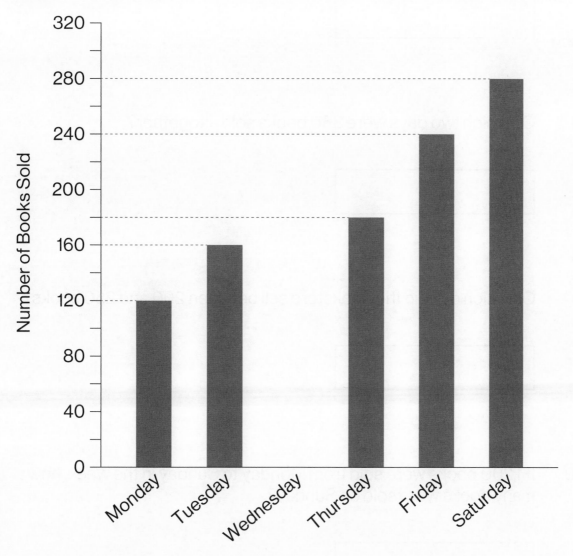

6.   On which of these six days was the bookstore closed?

Use the bar graph on the previous page to answer questions 7 to 10.

7. How many more books were sold on Saturday than on Thursday?

8. On which two days were 360 books sold altogether?

9. On which day did the bookstore sell between 200 and 250 books?

10. If 1,200 books were sold from Monday to Sunday in the week, how many books were sold on Sunday?

The bar graph below shows the amount of money Tiana saved over 5 months. Use it to answer questions 11 to 15 on this page and the following page.

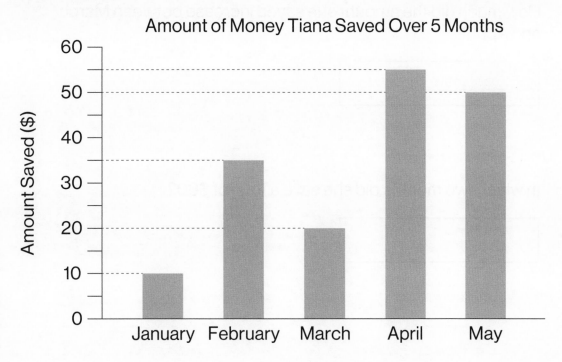

Amount of Money Tiana Saved Over 5 Months

11. In how many months did Tiana save less than $40?

12. In which month did she save $15 less than the previous month?

13. How much did she save over these 5 months?

Use the bar graph on the previous page to answer questions 14 and 15.

14. How much did the amount she saved increase between March and April?

```
┌─────────────────────────────┐
│                             │
│                             │
│                             │
└─────────────────────────────┘
```

15. In which two months did she save a total of $60?

```
┌─────────────────────────────┐
│                             │
│                             │
│                             │
└─────────────────────────────┘
```

Name: _____   Date: _____

Test B

20 min

Unit 10 Bar Graphs and Line Plots

Section A (2 points each)
Circle the correct option: **A**, **B**, **C**, or **D**.

The bar graph below shows the number of books bought by students at a book fair. Use it to answer questions 1 to 5 on this page and the following page.

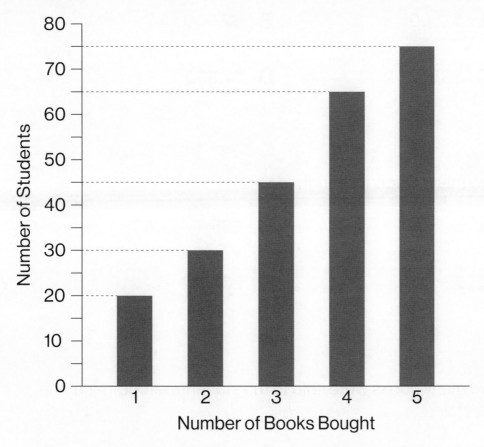

1.   How many students bought fewer than 3 books?

A 80   **B** 95   **C** 60   **D** 50

Use the bar graph on the previous page to answer questions 2 to 5.

2. How many students bought more than 2 books?

    A 20   **B** 30

    C 185   **D** 215

3. If each book cost $20, how much money was collected from the students who bought 5 books?

    A $1,500   **B** $2,000

    C $3,750   **D** $7,500

4. How many students bought books?

    A 5   **B** 235

    C 75   **D** 200

5. How many books were sold to the students altogether at the book fair?

    A 850   **B** 830

    C 375   **D** 215

Section B (2 points each)

The bar graph below shows the number of ice-cream cones sold by a store last week. Use the graph to answer questions 6 to 10 on this page and the following page.

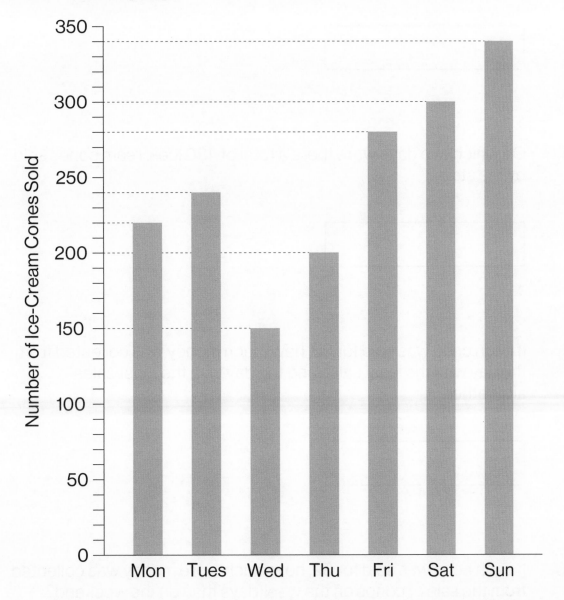

6.   How many days last week did the store sell more than 250 ice-cream cones per day?

Use the bar graph on the previous page to answer questions 7 to 10.

7. On which day was the sale of ice-cream cones double that of Wednesday?

8. On which two days were there a total of 430 ice-cream cones sold by the store?

9. If each cone was sold for $2, how much money was collected from the day with the least sales and the day with the most sales altogether?

10. If each cone was sold for $2, how much more money was collected from the sale of cones on the weekdays than on the weekend?

The table below shows the weight in pounds of bags of grapes sold in a store. Use it to answer questions 11 to 15 on this page and the following page.

$3\frac{1}{4}$	$2\frac{3}{4}$	$3\frac{1}{2}$	$3\frac{1}{2}$	$3\frac{3}{4}$	$3\frac{1}{4}$	$3\frac{3}{4}$	$3\frac{1}{2}$	$3\frac{1}{2}$
4	$3\frac{1}{2}$	$3\frac{1}{2}$	$3\frac{1}{4}$	4	$3\frac{1}{2}$	$2\frac{3}{4}$	$3\frac{3}{4}$	$2\frac{1}{2}$
4	$3\frac{1}{2}$	$2\frac{3}{4}$	$3\frac{3}{4}$	4	$3\frac{1}{4}$	$3\frac{3}{4}$	$3\frac{1}{2}$	

11.   Create a line plot.

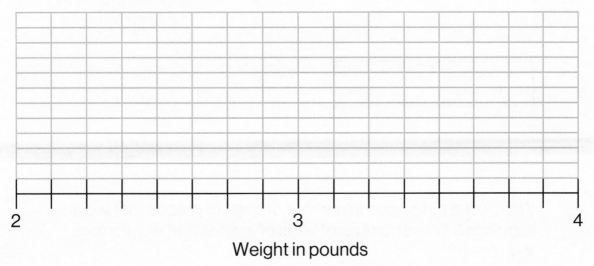

Weight in pounds

12.   How many bags of grapes are there altogether?

Refer to the table and line plot on the previous page to answer questions 13 to 15.

13. What is the most common weight of a bag of grapes?

14. How many bags of grapes weigh more than 4 lb?

15. What is the difference in number of bags of grapes that weigh less than 3 lb and number of bags of grapes that weigh more than 3.5 lb?

Name: _____ Date: _____

Test A **25 min** ⏰

Unit 11 Volume

Section A (2 points each)
Circle the correct option: **A**, **B**, **C**, or **D**.

1. How many unit cubes are in this solid?

    A 2

    B 3

    C 4

    D 6

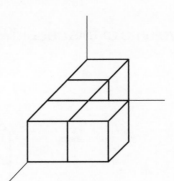

2. How many more unit cubes are needed to build Solid B from Solid A?

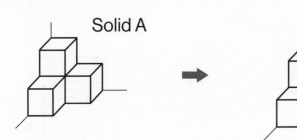

    A 3   **B** 4

    C 5   **D** 6

3. How many cubes need to be removed from the solid on the left to get the solid on the right?

A 2   **B** 3   **C** 1   **D** 4

4. What is the volume of this cuboid?

A 6 cm³

B 7 cm³

C 12 cm³

D 4 cm³

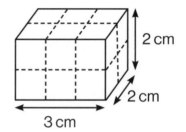

5. What is the volume of this cuboid?

A 24 cm³

B 12 cm³

C 15 cm³

D 96 cm³

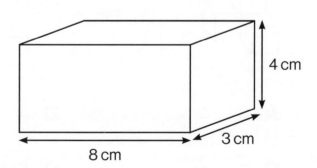

Section B (2 points each)

6. How many unit cubes were used to build this solid?

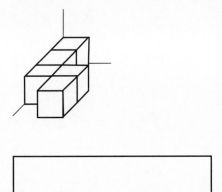

```
┌─────────────────────────────┐
│                             │
│                             │
│                             │
└─────────────────────────────┘
```

7. How many unit cubes were used to build this solid?

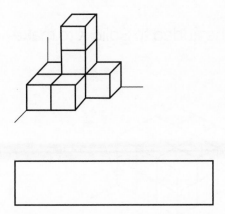

```
┌─────────────────────────────┐
│                             │
│                             │
│                             │
└─────────────────────────────┘
```

8. How many unit cubes are in this solid?

```
┌─────────────────────────────┐
│                             │
│                             │
│                             │
└─────────────────────────────┘
```

9. How many unit cubes are in this solid?

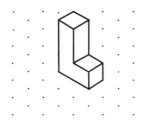

[   ]

10. How many **more** unit cubes must be added to Solid X to make Solid Y?

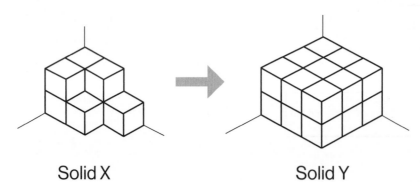

Solid X   Solid Y

[   ]

11. The solid below is made up of 1-cm cubes. Fill in the blanks.

Length = _____

Width = _____

Height = _____

Volume = _____

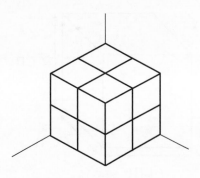

12. The solid shown below is made up of 1-cm cubes. What is the volume of the solid?

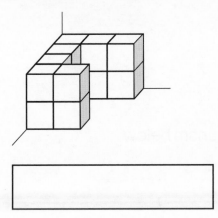

13. Find the volume of the cuboid below.

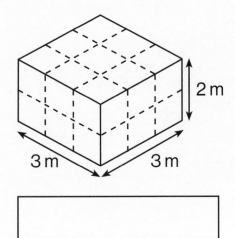

14. The figure below is a cube with 7-cm edges. What is its volume?

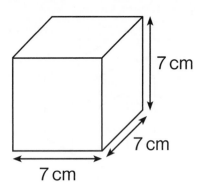

7 cm

7 cm

7 cm

15. Find the volume of the rectangular prism below.

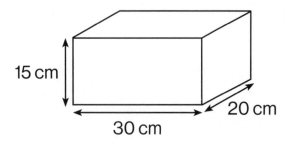

15 cm

30 cm

20 cm

Name: _____ Date: _____

Test B  25 min

30

Score

Unit 11 Volume

Section A (2 points each)
Circle the correct option: **A**, **B**, **C**, or **D**.

1. How many unit cubes are in this solid?

    A 8

    B 9

    C 12

    D 14

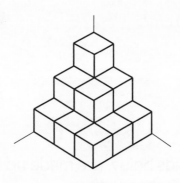

2. How many **more** unit cubes must be added to Solid A to make Solid B?

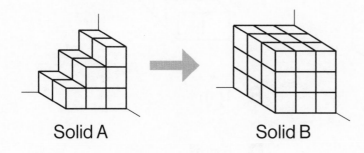

    Solid A   Solid B

    A 6   **B** 9   **C** 15   **D** 18

3.   The solid below is made up of 1-cm cubes. What is the volume of the solid?

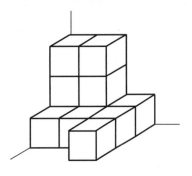

A 8 cm³

B 9 cm³

C 10 cm³

D 11 cm³

4.   The solids below are made up of 1-cm cubes. Find the difference in volume between them.

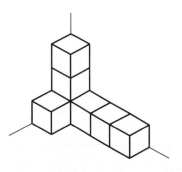 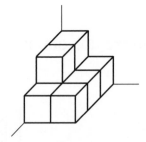

A 3 cm³

B 1 cm³

C 15 cm³

D 5 cm³

5. Stacie has 6 unit cubes. Which of these solids does she **not** have enough cubes to build?

A

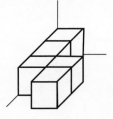

B

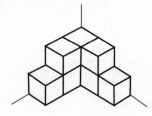

C

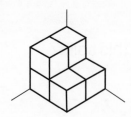

D

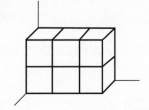

Section B (2 points each)

6. How many unit cubes were used to build this solid?

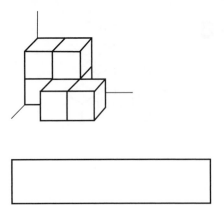

7. How many unit cubes were used to build this solid?

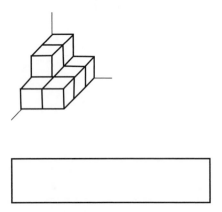

8. How many unit cubes are in this solid?

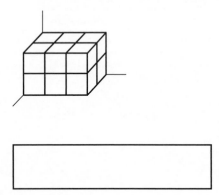

9. How many unit cubes are in this solid?

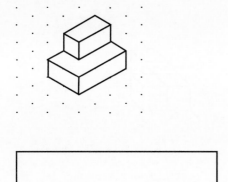

[ ]

10. Which one of the following solids can be made into a cuboid by adding three unit cubes to it?

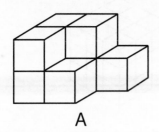

A

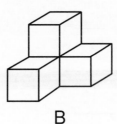

B

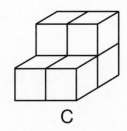

C

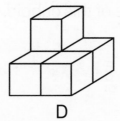

D

[ ]

11. How many cubes need to be removed from the solid on the left to form the solid on the right?

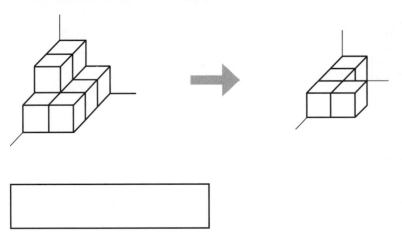

12. The solid below is made up of 1-cm cubes. Fill in the blanks.

Length = _____

Width = _____

Height = _____

Volume = _____

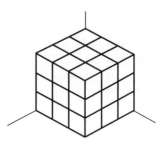

13. Find the volume of this cuboid.

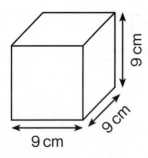

9 cm

9 cm

9 cm

14. How many 1-cm cubes can be packed into this box measuring 6 cm by 4 cm by 3 cm?

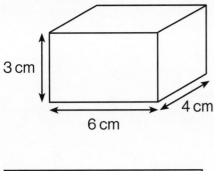

3 cm

6 cm

4 cm

15. A water tank measures 18 in. by 12 in. by 14 in. How many cubic inches of water can the tank hold when it is completely full?

BLANK

Name: _____   Date: _____

Test A   75 min

Year-End Assessment

Section A (2 points each)
Circle the correct option: **A**, **B**, **C**, or **D**.

1.   The sum of the values of the digit 5 in 57,382 and 34,569 is __?__.

    A 50,000   **B** 50,500

    C 5,050   **D** 550

2.   The difference between 7 tenths and 5 hundredths is __?__.

    A 0.75   **B** 0.43

    C 0.70   **D** 0.65

3.   Which of the following is **not** a factor of 24?

    A 24   **B** 8

    C 1   **D** 48

4. What is $5.47 – 10 cents expressed as a fraction?

    A $5.37

    B $5\frac{37}{100}$ dollars

    C $5\frac{47}{100}$ dollars

    D $5.46

5. Which one of the following angles is equal to $\frac{1}{2}$-turn?

    A

    B

    C

    D

6. How many pairs of parallel lines are there in the figure below?

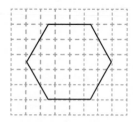

    A   1

    B   2

    C   0

    D   3

7. A chair costs \$28. A desk costs $\frac{4}{7}$ more than the chair.

    What is the cost of the desk?

    A \$16   **B** \$44

    C \$12   **D** \$76

8. The figure below shows a 5-cm square cut out from a rectangle.
    What is the perimeter of this figure?

    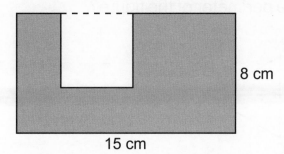

    8 cm

    15 cm

    A 33 cm   **B** 46 cm

    C 56 cm   **D** 61 cm

9. Anna is facing her school. If she turns clockwise to face south, how many degrees would she turn?

   A 90°

   B 180°

   C 270°

   D 360°

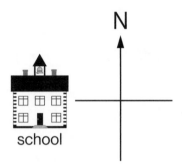

school

10. The figure below is made up of a rectangle and 2 identical triangles. XM = XP = 4 cm. What is the perimeter of the figure?

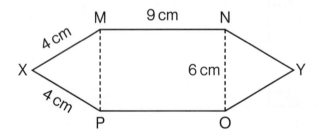

   A 25 cm

   B 34 cm

   C 40 cm

   D 46 cm

11.   How many more unit cubes are needed to build Solid B from Solid A?

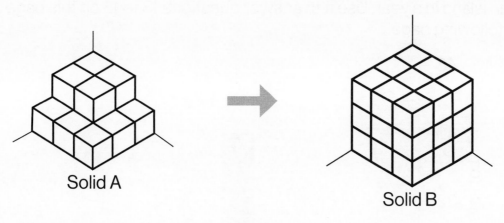

Solid A

Solid B

A 14   **B** 5

C 9   **D** 4

12.   How many lines of symmetry are drawn correctly for the figure below?

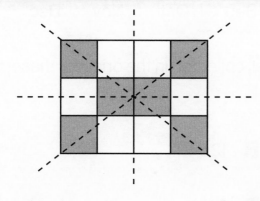

A 1   **B** 2

C 3   **D** 4

The graph below shows the amount of rainfall collected over six months on an island in a year. Use it to answer questions 13 to 15 on this page and the following page.

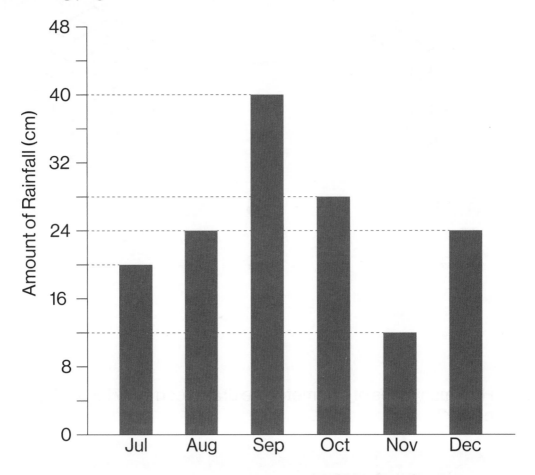

13. What was the amount of rainfall collected in the driest of these months?

A 40 cm **B** 12 cm

C 20 cm **D** 0 cm

Use the graph on the previous page to answer questions 14 and 15.

14. Between which two months did the amount of rainfall collected decrease by 16 cm?

  A Between Jul and Aug

  B Between Aug and Sep

  C Between Oct and Nov

  D Between Sep and Oct

15. In how many of these six months was the amount of rainfall collected less than 24 cm per month?

  A 2 months

  B 1 month

  C 3 months

  D none of the above

Section B (2 points each)

16. What is the sum of the 7th multiple of 8 and the 9th multiple of 6?

17. Fill in the blank with > , < or =.

$\$10.25$ _____ $10\frac{5}{25}$ dollars

18. What is the missing digit?

$$5.053 = 5 + \frac{\boxed{}}{10} + \frac{5}{100} + \frac{3}{1,000}$$

19. $16\frac{2}{50}$ expressed as a decimal is _____.

20. Shown below is rectangle ABCD. Find m ∠ADX.

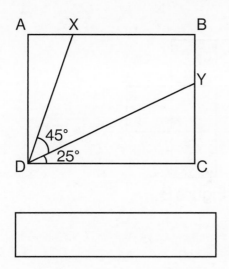

21. The figure below is made up of two squares.

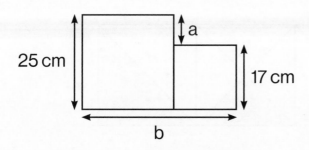

a) The marked length a is _____.

b) The marked length b is _____.

22. Both figures A and B are made up of 3-cm squares. What is the difference between their perimeters?

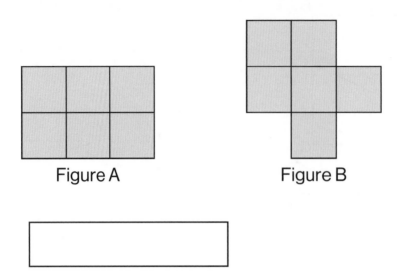

Figure A   Figure B

23. What fraction of this figure is shaded?

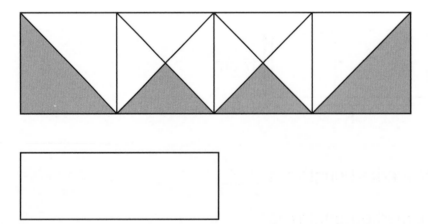

24. Draw a line perpendicular to line AB through point C.

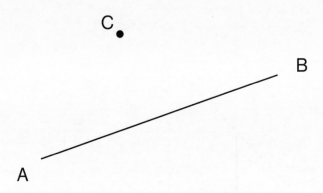

25. Measure the marked angle below.

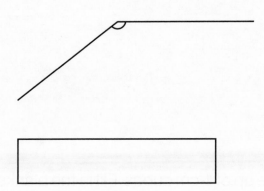

26. Express 15 minutes as a fraction of 2 hours. Give your answer in its simplest form.

27.   Complete the symmetric figure below.

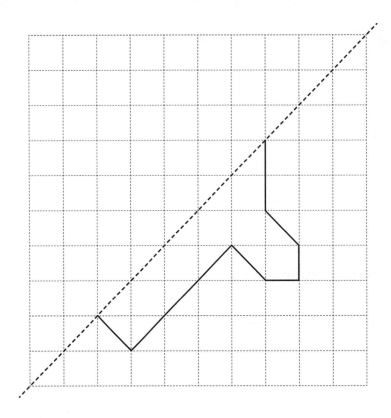

28.   The following solids are made up of 1-cm cubes. Fill in the blanks.

a)

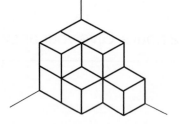

b)

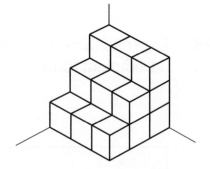

Volume: _____   Volume: _____

29. Find the value of the following expression.

$15 \div (3 + 2) \times (10 - 6)$

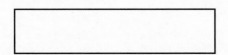

30. Malik bought a piece of wire $\frac{11}{12}$ m long. He used $\frac{3}{4}$ m of it to make a lantern. How many meters of wire did he have left? Express your answer in its simplest form.

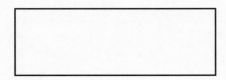

Section C (4 points each)

31. The capacity of Lakeisha's water bottle is 4 times the capacity of her cup. The total volume of water in her full water bottle and her full cup is 530 ml. How much more water is there in her water bottle than in her cup?

32. Andy cut a board into two pieces. One piece was $\frac{5}{12}$ m long and the other piece was $\frac{1}{6}$ m shorter. How long was the board at first?

33. Kumar used a bucket that can hold 5.07 L to pour water into an empty tank. He poured 7 full buckets of water into the tank. He then poured in an additional 3.01 L of water to fill the tank completely. What is the capacity of the tank?

34. A rectangular field measures 50 yd by 20 yd. What is the cost of building a fence around the entire field, if 1 yd of fence costs $9?

35. Fadiya ran once around a square field that is 45 yd long. Mikhail ran once around a field that is 50 yd long and 30 yd wide. Who ran a longer distance? How much longer?

Extra Credit

1. 2 pineapples cost the same as 3 mangoes. Arun paid $21 for 6 mangoes and 3 pineapples. What was the cost of each mango?

2. In the diagram below, the perimeter of Square A is 40 cm. Rectangle B has the same area as Square A. The difference between the length of Rectangle B and its width is 15 cm. What is the length and width of Rectangle B?

Square A

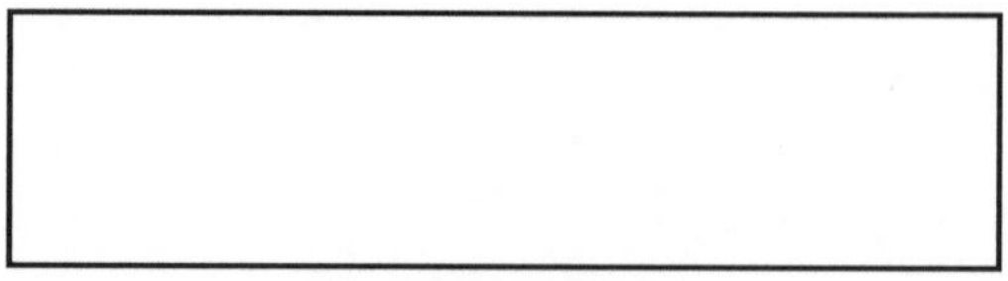

Rectangle B

Name: _____   Date: _____

Test B   **75 min**

Year-End Assessment

Section A (2 points each)
Circle the correct option: **A**, **B**, **C**, or **D**.

1. What is the sum of $\frac{2}{10}$ of $1 and $\frac{47}{100}$ of $1 ?

    A $0.49   **B** $0.67

    C $0.247   **D** $1.00

2. Which of the following has the smallest value?

    A $\frac{7}{10}$ **B** 0.42   **C** $\frac{84}{1,000}$ **D** 0.105

3. A piece of lace can be cut into equal pieces of length 6 cm or
    8 cm without any left over. Which of the following could be the
    length of the lace?

    A 12 cm   **B** 18 cm

    C 24 cm   **D** 36 cm

4. Which one of the following is the best estimate for 0.34 x 0.88?

    A 0.30 × 0.90   **B** 0.30 × 0.80

    C 0.40 × 0.90   **D** 0.40 × 0.80

5. $\frac{30}{9}$ expressed as a mixed number in its simplest form is:

    A $3\frac{1}{3}$ **B** $3\frac{3}{9}$ **C** $4\frac{1}{3}$ **D** $3\frac{2}{9}$

6. In the square shown below, m ∠*a* is twice m ∠*b*. Find m ∠*a*.

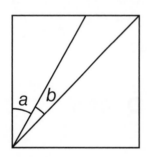

    A 15°   **B** 30°   **C** 45°   **D** 60°

7. What is the sum of 5 tenths and 17 hundredths?

    A 0.517   **B** 0.67

    C 5.17   **D** 6.7

8.　609.04 is 5 hundredths more than ___?___.

　　A 109.04　　　　　　**B** 608.54

　　C 608.99　　　　　　**D** 609.09

9.　Which one of the following angles is equal to $\frac{1}{2}$-turn?

A 　　　　**B**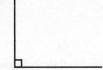

C 　　　　**D**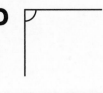

10.　4 pears cost $1.50. Mario gave the cashier a $20 bill for 20 pears.
　　How much change did he receive?

　　A $14　　　　　　**B** $12.50

　　C $7.50　　　　　　**D** $2.50

11. Which of the following is not an equivalent fraction of $\frac{6}{8}$?

    A $\frac{12}{16}$ **B** $\frac{3}{4}$ **C** $\frac{24}{32}$ **D** $\frac{4}{6}$

12. In the figure below, which line is perpendicular to CD?

    A DC

    B AB

    C AD

    D DE

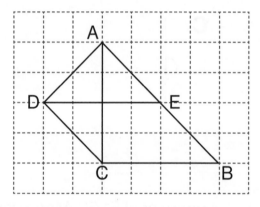

13. Which one of the following is a symmetric figure?

A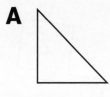

B

C

D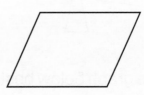

14. How many cubes need to be removed from the figure on the left to form the figure on the right?

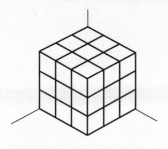

A 3

B 6

C 9

D 12

15. Jason was comparing the mass of 3 boxes as shown below.

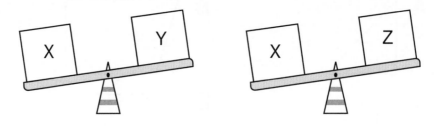

Which line graph below best represents the mass of the boxes?

A
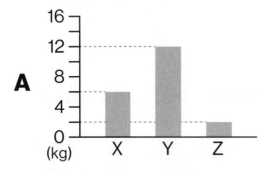

B
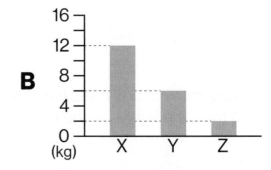

C
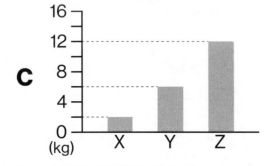

D
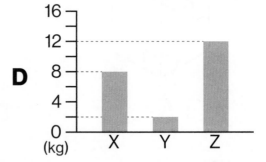

Section B (2 points each)

16. What is 16 ones, 3 tenths and 9 thousandths written as a number?

17. Solve the equation. Give your answer as a decimal.

$$3 + \frac{2}{5} + \frac{2}{25} =$$

18. Insert parentheses to make the following equation true.

$$2 \times 8 - 1 \div 2 = 7$$

19. The letters A and B each stand for a number on the number line below. What is the sum of A and B? Give your answer as a decimal.

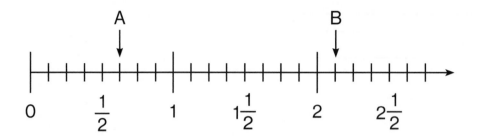

20. List the common factors of 12 and 21.

21. What number does the letter A represent on the number line below?

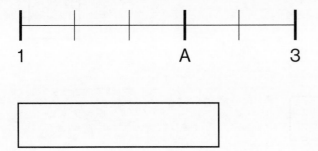

1   A   3

[ ]

22. Using a protractor, draw an angle equal to 250°.

23. Find the value of 1 ÷ 4 and round the answer to one decimal place.

[ ]

24. The figure to the right is made up of 2-cm squares. What is the perimeter of the figure?

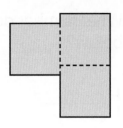

25. Look at the figure below.

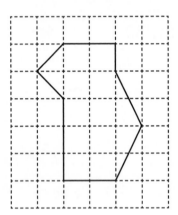

There are _____ obtuse angles inside the figure.

26. In the figure below, which line is parallel to FC?

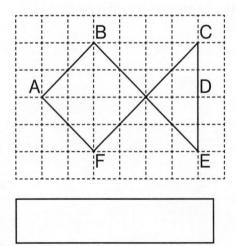

27. Shade two more squares in this figure so that AB is a line of symmetry.

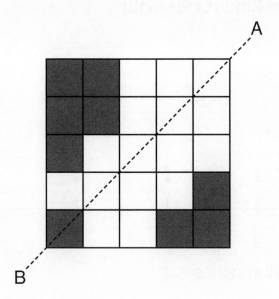

28. How many more squares must be shaded so that $\frac{2}{3}$ of the figure below is shaded?

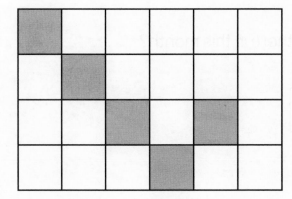

Use the line plot below to answer questions 29 and 30.

Rainfall in Cloud City in One Month

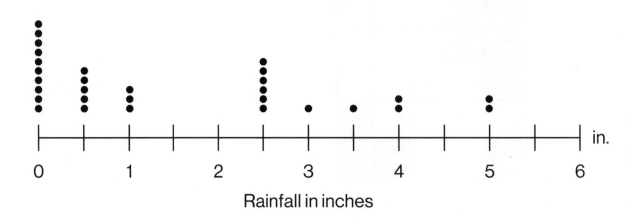

Rainfall in inches

29. How many days did the city receive rainfall between $1\frac{1}{2}$ in. and $4\frac{1}{2}$ in. within this month?

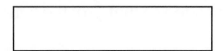

30. How many dry days were there in this month?

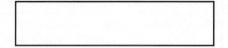

Section C (4 points each)

31. Ezekial has a total of 417 foreign stamps in his collection. He has 53 more Canadian stamps than Mexican stamps. He has twice as many French stamps as Mexican stamps.

    (a)   How many Mexican stamps does Ezekial have?

    (b)   How many Canadian stamps does Ezekial have?

32. Mrs. Reddy made some cookies. She sold $\frac{2}{5}$ of them and gave $\frac{1}{2}$ of of the remainder to her friends. If she had 60 cookies left, how many cookies did she sell?

33. Leslie has a piece of construction paper measuring 18 cm by 14 cm. She wants to cut out 3-cm squares from her construction paper. What is the maximum number of squares that Leslie can cut out?

34. It cost $2 per sq yd to plant grass. Wainani wants to plant new grass on her square lawn. How much will it cost her if her lawn has a perimeter of 84 yd?

35. Mei mixed 2 kg 500 g of white rice with 1 kg 700 g of brown rice.

    She cooked $\frac{1}{3}$ of the mixed rice. How much rice was left?

    Give your answer in kilograms and grams.

Extra Credit

1. Abdullah wants to buy 5 boxes of granola bars but he is short by $4.35. If he buys 3 boxes of granola bars instead, he will have $5.15 left. What is the cost of a box of granola bars?

2. This figure is made up of 4 identical rectangles.
The perimeter of each rectangle is 16 cm.
If the perimeter of the figure is 40 cm, what is the width of each rectangle?

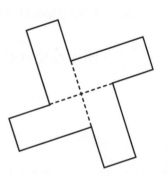

Answer Key and Detailed Solutions **4B**

Unit 6   Test A

1. A
2. C
3. D
4. D
5. A
6. B
7. C
8. D
9. A
10. B
11a. 0.17
11b. 3.1

12a. $1\dfrac{70}{100} = 1\dfrac{7}{10}$ dollars

12b. $4\dfrac{2}{100} = 4\dfrac{1}{50}$ dollars

13. $\dfrac{9}{10}$, nine tenths, 0.9

14.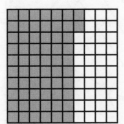

15. 50.46
16. 0.015
17a. $2.65
17b. $0.95
18. 7.209
19. $16\dfrac{3}{4}$

20a. $72.88
20b. $1.42
21. 0.6 and 1.4
22. 0.703, 0.307, 0.073
23. $3.605, 3\dfrac{3}{5}, 3.506, 3\dfrac{1}{4}$
24. 2.2, 2.5
25. 7.3 cm
26. 27.4 kg
27. 52.739
28. 1.6 cm
29. 2.6 L
30. $28

Unit 6 　 Test B

1. D

2. D

3. A

$$\frac{4}{5} = 0.8$$

$$\frac{3}{40} = 0.075$$

$$16 + \frac{4}{5} + \frac{3}{40} = 16.875$$

4. A

5. A

6. D

7. C

8. A

9. C

10. B

11.

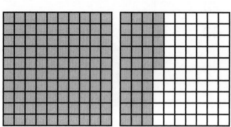

12. 2.036

13a. <

13b. >

14. 305

15a. $52.75

15b. 35.204

16a. 0.123

16b. 32.015

17. $6\frac{3}{4} = 6.75$

$6\frac{4}{5} = 6.8$

Answer: $6\frac{4}{5}, 6\frac{3}{4}, 6.705, 6.507$

18. $5\frac{21}{25}, 5\frac{17}{20}, 5.851, 6.001$

19a. 0.5

19b. 0.50

20. 22 tenths = 2.2
9 hundredths = 0.09
0.09 more than 2.2 is 2.29.
Answer: 2.29

21. 10.94 kg

22. $36.50

23.

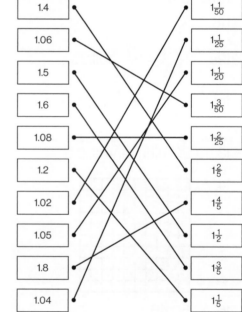

0.2 less than 4.37 is 4.17.
Answer: 4.17

24.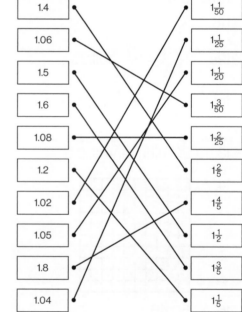

25. $\frac{5}{8} + 2\frac{1}{8} = 2\frac{6}{8} = 2\frac{3}{4} = 2.75$

Answer: 2.75

26a. 55

26b. 54.7

26c. 54.73

27. Round 3.995 to the nearest whole
number, tenth and hundredth, the
value is always 4.
Answer: 3.995

28. In this number series, the numbers
increase by 0.3.
The missing numbers are: 3.8, 4.1,
4.4, 4.7, and 5.0.
Answer: 5 numbers

29. hundredths place: 7
tenths place: 0
ones place: 0 + 2 = 2
thousandths place: 7 − 2 = 5
Answer: 2.075

30. Arvind: 1.78 m
Justin: $1\frac{3}{4}$ = 1.75 m
Meiling: 1.80 m
Justin is the shortest.
Meiling is the tallest.

Unit 7 — Test A

1. C

2. B

3. A

4. D

5. C

6. A
$83.2 + 100 = 183.2$
$183.2 - 2.8 = 180.4$
Answer: 180.4

7. B
$17.8 \times 5 = 89$
$89 \div 4 = 22.25$
Answer: 22.25

8. C
$1\frac{1}{4} = 1.25$
$3.2 + 1.25 = 4.45$ liters

9. B
$7 \times 1.05 = 7.35$ kg

10. A
$\$24.32 \div 4 = \$6.08$

11. $8.96 + 0.7 = 9.66$
Answer: 9.66

12. $3.3 - 0.09 = 3.21$
Answer: 3.21

13. $\$3.40 + \$0.75 = \$4.15$
Answer: $4.15

14. $\$9.50 - \$4.70 = \$4.80$
Answer: $4.80

15. $0.7 \times 12 = 8.4$
Answer: 8.4

16. $32 \div 7 = 4.57$
Answer: 4.6

17. 0.08

18. $0.21 \div 3 = 0.07$
Answer: 0.07

19. $\$32.15 + \$17.85 = \$50$
Answer: A and D

20. $\$7.45 \times 8 = \$59.60 \approx \$60$
Answer: $60

21. $10.08 \div 3 = 3.36$ m
Answer: 3.36 m

22. $2 \times \$3.05 = \$6.10$
$\$20 - \$6.10 = \$13.90$
Answer: $13.90

23. $3 \times 1.4 = 4.2$
$10 - 4.2 = 5.8$ kg
Answer: 5.8 kg

24. $5 - 0.96 = 4.04$
$4.04 \div 4 = 1.01$ L
Answer: 1.01 L

25. $24 \div 6 = 4$
$4 \times \$5.80 = \$23.20$
Answer: $23.20

Unit 7   Test B

1. A
    $2.45 \times 3 = 7.35$

2. B
    $0.74 \div 5 = 0.148 \approx 0.1$

3. A

4. C

5. A

6. B
    $25 - 0.96 = 24.04$ kg
    $24.04 \div 4 = 6.01$ kg

7. C
    $0.4 \times 6 = 2.4$ m
    $0.8 \times 5 = 4$ m
    $2.4 + 4 = 6.4$ m

8. A
    List the possible combinations of
    the 5 coins and the corresponding
    total amount.
    $5 \times 25¢ \longrightarrow \$1.25$
    $4 \times 25¢ + 1 \times 5¢ \longrightarrow \$1.05$
    $3 \times 25¢ + 2 \times 5¢ \longrightarrow \$0.85$
    $2 \times 25¢ + 3 \times 5¢ \longrightarrow \$0.65$
    $1 \times 25¢ + 4 \times 5¢ \longrightarrow \$0.45$
    $5 \times 5¢ \longrightarrow \$0.25$

9. B
    Work backwards.
    $20.05 - 4.75 = 15.3$
    $15.3 \div 3 = 5.1$

10. D
    Number of boxes of chocolates in
    a set $= 2 + 1 = 3$
    8 boxes $\div 3$ boxes $= 2$ R 2
    Number of sets of chocolates
    needed $= 2 + 1 = 3$ sets
    Cost per set $= 2 \times \$7.05 = \$14.10$
    3 sets $\times \$14.10 = \$42.30$

11. $52.7 - 6.9 = 45.8$
    $45.8 \div 2 = 22.9$
    Answer: 22.9

12. $0.2 - 0.02 = 0.18$
    Answer: 0.18

13. $2 - 0.45 - 0.6 = 0.95$ L
    Answer: 0.95 L

14. $\$4.55 + \$5.35 + \$5.45 = \$15.35$
    Answer: A, B, and D

15. $2.8 + \dfrac{3}{4} = 2.8 + 0.75$
    $\phantom{2.8 + \dfrac{3}{4}} = 3.55$ km
    Answer: 3.55 km

16. $20 \div 5 = 4$
    $4 \times \$3.80 = \$15.20$
    Answer: $15.20

17. $18 \div 2 = 9$
    $9 \times 0.78 = 7.02$
    Answer: 7.02 m

18. $204 - 61.2 = 142.8$ kg
    142.8 kg $\div 3 = 47.6$ kg
    $2 \times 47.6 = 95.2$ kg
    Answer: 95.2 kg

19. $549 \times \$7 = \$3,843 \approx \$3,840$
    Answer: $3,840

20. $\$4.95 \approx \$5$
    $\$20 \div \$5 = 4$
    Answer: 4

21. $10.1 \div 5 = 2.02$
    $2.02 \times 4 = 8.08$ m
    Answer: 8.08 m

22. $20 - 14 = 6$
    $\$7.80 \div 6 = \$1.30$
    $20 \times \$1.30 = \$26$
    Answer: $26

23. Restate the problem.
    $1 C + 1 P \longrightarrow 4.6$ lb
    So, $2 C + 2 P \longrightarrow 2 \times 4.6 = 9.2$ lb
    $2 P \longrightarrow 12.6 - 9.2 = 3.4$ lb
    $1 P \longrightarrow 3.4 \div 2 = 1.7$ lb
    Answer: 1.7 lb

24. $2 \times \$1.40 = \$2.80$
$\$23.80 - \$2.80 = \$21$
$\$21 \div \$3 = 7$
$7 + 2 = 9$
Answer: 9 smoothies

25. 1 bottle = 2 glasses
3 bottles = 6 glasses
2 glasses + 3 bottles =
2 glasses + 6 glasses = 8 glasses
$4.16 \div 8 = 0.52$ (a glass)
$2 \times 0.52 = 1.04$ (a bottle)
Answer: 1.04 L

1. B

2. C

3. B

4. D

5. D

6. D

7. A

8. B

9. C

10. B

   3 dimes $= \frac{3}{10}$ of \$1

   4 dollars 3 dimes $= 4 + \frac{3}{10} =$

   $4\frac{3}{10}$ dollars

11. A

    $1 - 0.06 = 0.94$

12. A

    $7 \times \$2.60 = \$18.20$

13. C

    $\$4.20 \div 7 = \$0.60$

14. B

    $3 \times \$1.50 = \$4.50$

    $3 \times 8 = 24$

15. C

    $5 \times \$1.50 = \$7.50$

    $\$20 - \$7.50 = \$12.50$

16. hundredths

17. 4.057, 4.075, 4.507, 4.705

18. 0.24

19. 10.234

20. $8.99 + 0.02 = 9.01$

    Answer: 9.01

21. 3.3

22. $\frac{125}{1,000} = \frac{1}{8}$

23. 35

24. $5 \div 7 = 0.71$

    Answer: 0.7

25. \$0.25

26. $\$10.45 \times 7 = \$73.15$

    $\$73.15 \approx \$73$

    Answer: \$73

27. 50

28. $4 \div 8 = 0.5$

    $5 \times 0.5 = 2.5$

    Answer: 2.5

29. 1.6 qt

30. $0.38 \times 6 = 2.28$

    $2.28 + 3.55 = 5.83$ yd

    Answer: 5.83 yd

31.

    $\$33.20 - \$4 - \$4 - \$3 = \$22.20$

    $\$22.20 \div 3 = \$7.40$ (Josef)

    $\$7.40 + \$4 + \$3 = \$14.40$ (Walter)

    Answer: \$14.40

32. $8 - 3 = 5$

    $\$8.75 \div 5 = \$1.75$

    $\$1.75 \times 8 = \$14$

    Answer: \$14

Extra Credit

1. $\$1.50 + \$3.50 = \$5$

   $\$5 \div 2 = \$2.50$

   Answer: \$2.50

2. Look for the pattern.
   The cost of each additional pen is \$0.40 more.
   Cost of 4 pens: \$1.90
   Cost of 5 pens: \$2.30
   Cost of 6 pens: \$2.70
   Answer: \$2.70

1. B

2. D

3. C

4. B

5. B

6. D

7. C

8. D

9. B

10. B
$4.5 \div 30 = 0.15$ kg
$4 \times 0.15 = 0.6$ kg

11. D

12. D
$3 \times 0.65 = 1.95$
$4 \times 0.50 = 2.00$
$\$1.95 + \$2.00 = \$3.95$

13. B
$250 \div 2.5 = 100$
$100 + 2.5 = 102.5$

14. B
$4 \times \dfrac{1}{8} = \dfrac{1}{2} = 0.5$
$2 \times 0.25 = 0.5$

15. C
$24 - 2.4 = 21.6$ m
$21.6 \div 2 = 10.8$ m
$10.8 + 2.4 = 13.2$ m

16. 0.12

17. 915

18. 6

19. 6.83

20. $5.6 - 0.08 = 5.52$
Answer: 5.52

21. 1.085

22. $3\dfrac{3}{4}, 3.7, 2\dfrac{5}{10}, 2.3$

23. 97.684, 97.68, <u>97.676</u>, 97.672, <u>97.668</u>, <u>97.664</u>

24. $7 - 3 = 4$
$4 \div 5 = 0.8$
$3 \times 0.8 = 2.4$
$3 + 2.4 = 5.4$
Answer: 5.4

25. $9.31 - 3.97 = 5.34$
$5.34 \div 6 = 0.89$
Answer: 0.89

26. $15.6 - 13.8 = 1.8$
$1.8 \div 0.3 = 6$
$6 - 1 = 5$
Answer: 5

27. $1\dfrac{1}{4} = 1.25$
$7.2 + 1.25 = 8.45$
Answer: 8.45 L

28. $21.8 - 3.6 = 18.2$
$18.2 \div 2 = 9.1$ m (shorter)
$9.1 + 3.6 = 12.7$ m (longer)
Answer: 12.7 m

29. $\$30 - \$15.80 = \$14.20$
$\$14.20 \div 2 = \$7.10$ (book)
$\$15.80 - \$7.10 = \$8.70$ (magazine)
Answer: $8.70

30. 1 roll = $47
5 sheets = $4.70 x 5 = $23.50
Total = $47 + $23.50 = $70.50
Change = $80 - $70.50 = $9.50
Answer: $9.50

31. $1.52 \times 2 = 3.04$
$2.75 \times 5 = 13.75$
$3.04 + 13.75 = 16.79$
$50 - 16.79 = 33.21$ yd
Answer: 33.21 yd

32. $2 \times \$1.50 = \$3$
$\$31.50 + \$3 = \$34.50$
$\$34.50 \div 5 = \$6.90$
Answer: $6.90

Extra Credit

1. 10 pineapples and 6 watermelons
    cost 2 times $35.75 = $71.50

    $71.50 − $55.90 = $15.60
    (3 pineapples)

    $15.60 ÷ 3 = $5.20
    (1 pineapple)

    $37.75 − (5 × $5.20) = $9.75
    (3 watermelon)

    $9.75 ÷ 3 = $3.25 (1 watermelon)

    $5.20 − $3.25 = $1.95

    Answer: $1.95

2.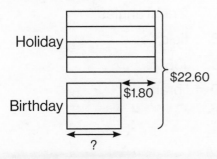

    4 × $1.80 = $7.20
    $22.60 − $7.20 = $15.40
    $15.40 ÷ 7 = $2.20
    Answer: $2.20

1.   C

2.   A

3.   B

4.   B
      $90° - 56° = 34°$

5.   C

6.   B

7.   B

8.   A

9.   A

10.   D

11.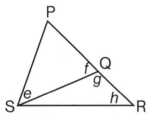

12.   L and M

13.   B is a square and a rectangle.
      C and E are rectangles.

14.

15. $90° - 53° = 37°$
      Answer: m $\angle a = 37°$

16. $90° - 35° = 55°$
      Answer: $55°$

17. $180° - 44° = 136°$

18a. $\angle DAB, \angle DCB$

18b. $\angle ADC, \angle ABC$

19.   b, c, a

20. $140°$

21.   B

22.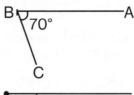

23.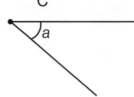

24a. 1, $90°$

24b. 2, $180°$

24c. 3, $270°$

25.   west

26.   south

27.   2 right angles

28.   field

29. $135°$

30.   library

1.   B

2.   D

3.   D

4.   D

5.   B
     $90° - 37° - 25° = 28°$

6.   A
     $180° - 36° - 90° = 54°$

7.   D

8.   A

9.   D

10. A

11. 45°

12.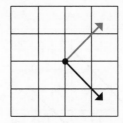

13. $\angle d$

14. A, B, C

15. C, D

16. A, C, D

17. m $\angle d = 90° - 49° = 41°$
     Answer: 41°

18. $180° - 140° = 40°$
     Answer: 40°

19. A•   •B

     C

20. 120°

21. 100°

22.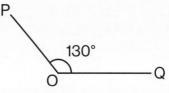

23. $1h = 360° = 4$ right angles
     Answer: 4

24. southwest

25a. 1, 90°

25b. 4, 360°

25c. $\frac{1}{4}$

26.

27. point A

28. point B

29. 7:30 p.m.

30. Work backwards.
     Before making a $\frac{1}{4}$-turn in the counterclockwise direction, he is facing the Coffee Shop.
     Before turning 135° in the clockwise direction, he is facing the Stadium.

     Answer: Stadium

1. C
2. B
3. C
4. D
5. C
6. C
7. A
8. C
9. B
10. C
11. b
12.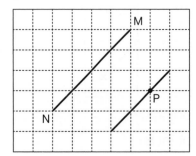
13. Answer: D

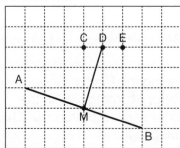

14. AB // ED
15. FK ⊥ EG
    EH ⊥ FG
16. C, D, E
17a.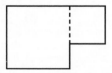

17b.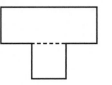

17c.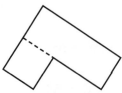

17d.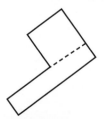

18.

Answer: 9

19. 27 - 5 - 14 = 8 cm
    Answer: 8 cm
20. 22 - 14 = 8 cm (DE)
    22 + 14 = 36 cm (BG)
    Answer: 8 cm, 36 cm
21. 6 + 6 + 5 = 17
    Answer: 17 cm
22. 13 in.
23. Equilateral, Isosceles, Scalene
24.

25.

26.

27.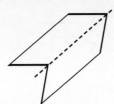

28.

29. A

30a.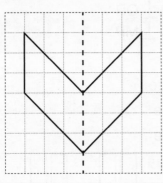

30b.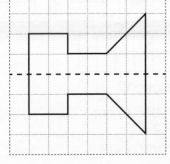

1. D

2. D

3. B

4. C

5. A

6. D

7. A

8. A

9. D

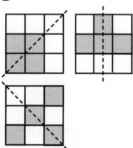

10. B

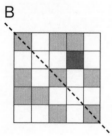

11. CD

12.

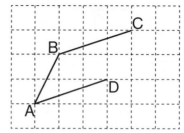

13a. B, C, D

13b. A, B, D

13c. B, D

14. $MN \perp NQ$
$MQ \perp QR$
$MQ \perp MP$

15a. True

15b. False

15c. True

15d. True

16.

17.

Answer: 12

18. 26 - 12 = 14 cm
14 ÷ 2 = 7
Answer: 7 cm

19. Unfold the rectangular card.
Length = 16 + 12 + 13 = 41 cm
Answer: 41 cm

20. 7 m, 11 m, 7 m

21. 18 ft

22. b, c

23.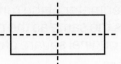

Answer: 2 lines of symmetry

24a.

24b.

24c.

24d.

24e.

24f.

25.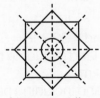

Answer: 4 lines of symmetry

26. D

27.

28.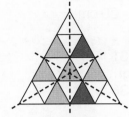

29.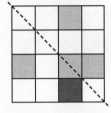

30a.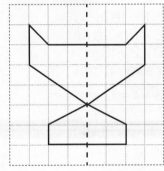

30b.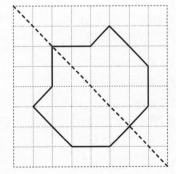

Unit 9 — Test A

1. B
   $64 \div 4 = 16$ cm

2. A
   $2 \times 30 = 60$ cm
   $100 - 60 = 40$ cm
   $40 \div 2 = 20$ cm

3. C
   $9 \times 9 = 81$
   So, length = 9 m
   $4 \times 9 = 36$ m

4. B
   Guess and Check.
   $8 \times 6 = 48$ cm^2
   $8 - 6 = 2$ cm
   So, length = 8 cm

5. C
   $9 + 5 = 14$ cm

6. $2 \times 8 = 16$ m
   $36 - 16 = 20$ m
   $20 \div 2 = 10$ m
   Answer: 10 m

7. $48 \div 4 = 12$ cm
   $12 \times 12 = 144$ cm^2
   Answer: 144 cm^2

8. $28 \div 4 = 7$ m
   $4 + 7 = 11$ m
   11 m $\times 2 = 22$ m
   Answer: 22 m

9. $10 \times 3 = 30$ cm^2
   Answer: 30 cm^2

10. $15 \times 15 = 225$ cm^2
    $225 \div 9 = 25$ cm
    Answer: 25 cm

11. $11 + 5 = 16$ cm
    $2 \times 16 = 32$ cm
    $32 \div 4 = 8$ cm
    Answer: 8 cm

12. The perimeter of the remaining card is the same as the perimeter of the original square card.

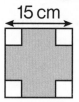

15 cm

$4 \times 15 = 60$ cm
Answer: 60 cm

13. 8 units $\longrightarrow$ 72 cm
    1 unit $\longrightarrow$ $72 \div 8 = 9$ cm
    3 units $\longrightarrow$ $3 \times 9 = 27$ cm
    Answer: 27 cm

14. $72 \div 4 = 18$ cm
    $18 \div 2 = 9$ cm
    $18 \times 9 = 162$ cm^2
    Answer: 162 cm^2

15. $4 \times 4 = 16$
    So, length of a rug = 4 m
    Perimeter of carpet = $4 \times 8 = 32$ m
    Answer: 32 m

16. $19 - 2 - 2 = 15$ m
    $16 - 2 - 2 = 12$ m
    $15 \times 12 = 180$ m^2
    Answer: 180 m^2

17. Area of floor = $20 \times 15 = 300$ m^2
    $15 - 5 - 3 = 7$
    $20 - 5 - 3 = 12$
    Area of carpet = $12 \times 7 = 84$ m^2
    $300 - 84 = 216$
    Answer: 216 m^2

18. Area of land = $32 \times 18 = 576$ m^2
    Length of land including path = 32 + 1 + 1 = 34 m
    Width of land including path = 18 + 1 + 1 = 20 m
    Area of land including path = 34 × 20 = 680 m^2
    Area of path = $680 - 576 = 104$ m^2
    Answer: 104 m^2

1. C
   $7 \times 7 = 49$
   So, length of square = 7 cm
   $14 + 7 = 21$ cm
   $7 \times 21 = 147$ cm^2

2. B
   The perimeter of the figure is the same as the perimeter of the surrounding rectangle.

   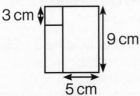

   3 cm
   9 cm
   5 cm

   $3 + 5 + 9 = 17$ cm
   $2 \times 17 = 34$ cm

3. A
   $14 - 6 = 8$ m
   $8 \times 8 = 64$ m^2
   $14 \times 12 = 168$ m^2
   $168 - 64 = 104$ m^2

4. D
   $4 \times 8 = 32$ cm
   $32 + 5 + 5 = 42$ cm

5. D
   $12 - 1 - 1 = 10$ m
   $10 - 1 - 1 = 8$ m
   $10 \times 8 = 80$ m^2

6. The perimeter of the figure is the same as the perimeter of the surrounding square.

   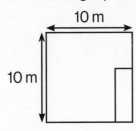

   10 m
   10 m

   $4 \times 10 = 40$ m
   Answer: 40 m

7. $20 - 4 - 4 = 12$ m
   $12 \times 12 = 144$ m^2
   $20 \times 16 = 320$ m^2
   $320 - 144 = 176$ m^2
   Answer: 176 m^2

8. Area of a unit square
   $= 2 \times 2 = 4$ cm^2
   Total area of 9 unit squares
   $= 9 \times 4 = 36$ cm^2
   Unshaded number of unit squares
   $= 8 \div 2 = 4$
   Unshaded area $= 4 \times 4 = 16$ cm^2
   $36 - 16 = 20$ cm^2
   Answer: 20 cm^2

9. 2 parts can form a square.
   Area of a square
   $= 2 \times 32 = 64$ m^2
   $8 \times 8 = 64$
   So, width of garden = 8 m
   Length of garden $= 2 \times 8 = 16$ m
   Answer: 16 m

10. The perimeter of the figure is the same as the perimeter of the surrounding square.

    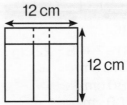

    12 cm
    12 cm

    $4 \times 12 = 48$ cm
    Answer: 48 cm

11. $16 + 2 + 2 = 20$ m
    $20 \times 2 = 40$ m^2
    $10 \times 2 = 20$ m^2
    $40 + 20 = 60$ m^2
    $2 \times 60 = 120$ m^2
    Answer: 120 m^2

12. $3 \times 3 = 9$
     So, length of A = 3 m
     $7 \times 7 = 49$
     So, length of C = 7 m
     $3 + 7 = 10$ m
     $10 \times 10 = 100$ m^2
     Answer: 100 m^2

13. The area of the figure is the same
     as the area of 2 and a half squares.
     $20 \times 20 = 400$ cm^2
     $400 \div 2 = 200$ cm^2
     $400 + 400 + 200 = 1{,}000$ cm^2
     Answer: 1,000 cm^2

14. The perimeter of the figure is
     the same as the perimeter of the
     surrounding rectangle.

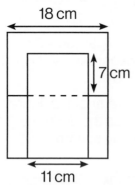

     Width = $11 - 7 + 18 = 22$ cm
     $18 + 22 = 40$ cm
     $2 \times 40 = 80$ cm
     Answer: 80 cm

15. Unfold the paper.

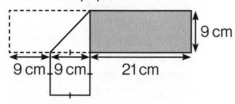

     Length = $21 + 9 + 9 = 39$ cm
     $39 \times 9 = 351$ cm^2
     Answer: 351 cm^2

16. Area of paper
     $= 14 \times 11 = 154$ cm^2
     Length of photograph
     $= 14 - 2 - 2 = 10$ cm
     Width of photograph
     $= 11 - 2 - 2 = 7$ cm
     Area of photograph
     $= 10 \times 7 = 70$ cm^2
     Area of border
     $= 154 - 70 = 84$ cm^2
     Answer: 84 cm^2

17. Perimeter of field = $55 + 25 + 55$
     $+25 = 160$ yd
     $800 \div 160 = 5$
     Laila has to walk 5 times around
     the field.

18a. Perimeter of remaining cardboard
     = perimeter of cardboard +
     2 sides of small square
     $= 24 + 18 + 24 + 18 + 10 + 10$
     $= 104$ cm
     Answer: 104 cm

18b. Area of cardboard
     $= 24 \times 18 = 432$ cm^2
     Area of square
     $= 10 \times 10 = 100$ cm^2
     Area of remaining cardboard
     $= 432 - 100 = 332$ cm^2
     Answer: 332 cm^2

Unit 10 · Test A

1. D

2. B

3. B

4. C
$350 − $150 = $200

5. A
$200 + $250 + $350 + $150 + $200 = $1,150

6. No books were sold on Wednesday.
Answer: Wednesday

7. 280 − 180 = 100
Answer: 100 more books

8. 120 + 240 = 360
Answer: Monday and Friday

9. Friday

10. 120 + 160 + 0 + 180 + 240 + 280 = 980
1,200 − 980 = 220
Answer: 220 books

11. 3

12. $35 − $20 = $15
Answer: March

13. $10 + $35 + $20 + $55 + $50 = $170
Answer: $170

14. $55 − $20 = $35
Answer: $35

15. January and May

Unit 10 · Test B

1. D   20 + 30 = 50

2. C   45 + 65 + 75 = 185

3. D   75 × 5 = 375
375 × $20 = $7,500

4. B
20 + 30 + 45 + 65 + 75 = 235

5. A
20 × 1 = 20
30 × 2 = 60
45 × 3 = 135
65 × 4 = 260
75 × 5 = 375
20 + 60 + 135 + 260 + 375 = 850

6. More than 250 cones were sold on Friday, Saturday, and Sunday.
Answer: 3 days

7. Saturday

8. 150 + 280 = 430
Answer: Wednesday and Friday

9. 150 × $2 = $300
340 × $2 = $680
$300 + $680 = $980
Answer: $980

10. 220 + 240 + 150 + 200 + 280 = 1,090
300 + 340 = 640
1,090 − 640 = 450
450 × $2 = $900
Answer: $900

11.
Weight of Bags of Grapes

12. 26

13. $3\frac{1}{2}$ lb

14. 0

15. 9 − 4 = 5
Answer: 5

Unit 11   Test A

1. C
2. B
3. A
4. C
5. D
6. 5
7. 7
8. 4
9. 4
10. $18 - 8 = 10$
    Answer: 10 more cubes
11. Length = 2 cm
    Width = 2 cm
    Height = 2 cm
    Volume = 8 cm^3
12. $14 \times 1\,\text{cm}^3 = 14\,\text{cm}^3$
    Answer: 14 cm^3
13. $3 \times 3 \times 2 = 18\,\text{m}^3$
14. $7 \times 7 \times 7 = 343\,\text{cm}^3$
    Answer: 343 cm^3
15. $30 \times 20 \times 15 = 9{,}000\,\text{cm}^3$

Unit 11   Test B

1. D
2. C
    $27 - 12 = 15$
3. D
4. B
5. B
6. 6
7. 8
8. 12
9. 8
10. D
11. 4
12. Length = 3 cm
    Width = 3 cm
    Height = 3 cm
    Volume = 27 cm^3
13. $9 \times 9 \times 9 = 729\,\text{cm}^3$
14. $6 \times 4 \times 3 = 72$
    Answer: 72 1-cm cubes
15. $18 \times 12 \times 14 = 3{,}024\,\text{in.}^3$
    Answer: 3,024 in.^{3}

1. B

2. D
   $0.7 - 0.05 = 0.65$

3. D

4. B

5. C

6. D

7. B
   $\frac{4}{7} \times \$28 = \$16$
   $\$28 + \$16 = \$44$

8. C
   $15 + 8 = 23$ cm
   $2 \times 23 = 46$ cm
   $46 + 5 + 5 = 56$ cm

9. C
   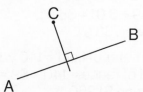

10. B
    $4 + 4 + 4 + 4 + 9 + 9 = 34$ cm

11. A

12. B

13. B

14. C

15. A

16. $56 + 54 = 110$
    Answer: 110

17. $\$10\frac{5}{25} = \$10\frac{20}{100} = \$10.20$
    $\$10.25 > \$10.20$
    Answer: >

18. 0

19. 16.04

20. 20°

21a. $25 - 17 = 8$
     Answer: 8 cm

21b. $25 + 17 = 42$
     Answer: 42 cm

22. $10 \times 3 = 30$ cm (A)
    $12 \times 3 = 36$ cm (B)
    $36 - 30 = 6$
    Answer: 6 cm

23. $\frac{3}{8}$

24.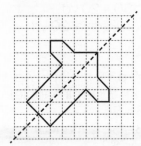

25. 143°

26. $\frac{15}{120} = \frac{3}{24} = \frac{1}{8}$

27.

28a. 8 cm³

28b. 18 cm³

29. $15 \div 5 \times 4 = 3 \times 4 = 12$
    Answer: 12

30. $\frac{11}{12} - \frac{3}{4} = \frac{2}{12} = \frac{1}{6}$
    Answer: $\frac{1}{6}$ m

31. Water bottle ⎱ 530 ml
    Cup   ?

    5 units = 530 ml
    1 unit = 530 ÷ 5 = 106 ml
    3 units = 3 × 106 = 318 ml
    Answer: There is 318 ml more
    water in her water bottle than in
    her cup.

32. $\frac{5}{12} - \frac{1}{6} = \frac{3}{12}$ m

    $\frac{5}{12} + \frac{3}{12} = \frac{8}{12} = \frac{2}{3}$ m

    The wire was $\frac{2}{3}$ m long at first.

    Answer: $\frac{2}{3}$ m

33. $5.07 \times 7 = 35.49$
    $35.49 + 3.01 = 38.5$ L
    Answer: 38.5 L

34. Perimeter of field = 140 yd
    Cost of fence = 140 × $9 = $1,260
    Answer: $1,260

35. 45 × 4 = 180 yd (Fadiya)
    50 + 30 + 30 + 50 = 160 yd
    (Mikhail)
    180 − 160 = 20 yd
    Answer: Fadiya, 20 yd

Extra Credit

1. 6 m + 3 p = 4 p + 3 p = 7 p
   $21 ÷ 7 = $3 (a pineapple)
   2 × $3 = $6
   $6 ÷ 3 = $2 (a mango)
   Answer: $2

2. Length of A = 40 ÷ 4 = 10 cm
   Area of A = 10 × 10 = 100 cm^2
   Use guess and check strategy.
   20 × 5 = 100
   20 − 5 = 15
   Length of B = 20 cm
   Width of B = 5 cm
   Answer: 20 cm, 5 cm

1. B

2. C

3. C
   None of the other options can be divded by both 6 and 8.

4. A

5. A

6. B

7. B
   $0.5 + 0.17 = 0.67$

8. C
   $0.05 + 608.99 = 609.04$

9. C
   $\frac{1}{2}$–turn = 180°

10. B
    $20 \div 4 = 5$
    $5 \times \$1.50 = \$7.50$
    $\$20 - \$7.50 = \$12.50$

11. D
    $\frac{12}{16} = \frac{3}{4}$ $\frac{24}{32} = \frac{3}{4}$ $\frac{4}{6} = \frac{2}{3}$

12. C

13. A

14. C

15. B
    Box Z is the lightest.
    Box X is the heaviest.

16. 16.309

17. $\frac{2}{5} = 0.4$

    $\frac{2}{25} = 0.08$

    $3 + \frac{2}{5} + \frac{2}{25} = 3.48$

    Answer: 3.48

18. $2 \times (8 - 1) \div 2 = 7$

19. $\frac{5}{8} + 2\frac{1}{8} = 2\frac{6}{8} = 2\frac{3}{4} = 2.75$
    Answer: 2.75

20. 1, 3

21. $3 - 1 = 2$
    $2 \div 5 = 0.4$
    $3 \times 0.4 = 1.2$
    $1 + 1.2 = 2.2$
    Answer: 2.2

22.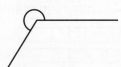

23. $1 \div 4 = 0.25 \approx 0.3$
    Answer: 0.3

24.

    $8 \times 2 = 16$ cm
    Answer: 16 cm

25. 5 obtuse angles

26. AB // FC
    Answer: AB

27.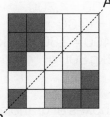

28. $\frac{2}{3} \times 24 = 16$
    $16 - 5 = 11$
    Answer: 11

29. 10

30. 10

31a.

Canadian

Mexican 53

French

417

$417 - 53 = 364$
4 units = 364
1 unit = $364 \div 4 = 91$
Answer: 91 Mexican stamps

31b. $91 + 53 = 144$
Answer: 144 Canadian stamps

32.

Remainder
60

3 units: 60
1 unit: $60 \div 3 = 20$
4 units: $4 \times 20 = 80$
Answer: 80

33. $18 \div 3 = 6$
$14 \div 3 = 4 \, R \, 2$
$6 \times 4 = 24$
Answer: 24 squares

34. Length of lawn = $84 \div 4 = 21$ yd
Area of lawn = $21 \times 21 = 441$ yd^2
Cost = $441 \times \$2 = \$882$
Answer: It will cost $882.

35. $2,500 + 1,700 = 4,200$
$4,200 \div 3 = 1,400$
$4,200 - 1,400 = 2,800 = 2$ kg 800 g
Answer: 2 kg 800 g

Extra Credit

1. Cost of 2 boxes of granola bars =
$\$4.35 + \$5.15 = \$9.50$
$\$9.50 \div 2 = \$4.75$
Answer: $4.75

2. 4×16 cm = 64 cm
64 cm − 40 cm = 24 cm
24 cm $\div$ 8 = 3 cm
Answer: 3 cm